A Superfluid Universe

A Superfluid Universe

Kerson Huang

MIT

World Scientific

NEW JERSEY · LONDON · SINGAPORE · BEIJING · SHANGHAI · HONG KONG · TAIPEI · CHENNAI · TOKYO

Published by

World Scientific Publishing Co. Pte. Ltd.

5 Toh Tuck Link, Singapore 596224

USA office: 27 Warren Street, Suite 401-402, Hackensack, NJ 07601

UK office: 57 Shelton Street, Covent Garden, London WC2H 9HE

Library of Congress Cataloging-in-Publication Data

Names: Huang, Kerson, 1928–   author.

Title: A superfluid universe / Kerson Huang, Massachusetts Institute of Technology, USA.

Description: Hackensack, NJ : World Scientific, [2016] |
    Includes bibliographical references and index.

Identifiers: LCCN 2016030571| ISBN 9789813148451 (hardcover ; alk. paper) |
    ISBN 9813148454 (hardcover ; alk. paper)

Subjects: LCSH: Superfluidity. | Matter--Properties. | Quantum theory.

Classification: LCC QC175.4 .H83 2016 | DDC 523.01--dc23

LC record available at https://lccn.loc.gov/2016030571

British Library Cataloguing-in-Publication Data

A catalogue record for this book is available from the British Library.

Preface

Newton's physics was "natural philosophy", and he inquired into everything — optics, acoustics, gravity. As physics develops, subdivisions will appear that require dedicated effort to master, and so physicists specialize. Enrico Fermi was perhaps the last physicist to do both theory and experiment effectively, proposing "the universal Fermi interaction" of beta-decay, on the one hand, and discovering the Δ particle on the other. It has now become difficult to be a generalist even in theoretical physics. You could be a particle theorist, cosmologist, or condensed matter theorist, but rarely all three! Even in particle theory, you would specialize in QCD, or electroweak theory, and in QCD you might specialize in confinement, lattice QCD, or quark-gluon plasma.

Nature, however, does not know about our subdivisions, and exhibits phenomena that cut across all our specialties. I find such a situation in the great puzzles of our time: dark energy and dark matter. These phenomena may find explanations in the fact that the Higgs field of particle theory, and/or an extension of it, fills all space, making the whole universe a superfluid, by virtue of the dynamics of its quantum phase. In short, we propose that dark energy is the energy density of the superfluid, and dark matter is the deviation of the superfluid density from its equilibrium value. While particle physics is concerned with scales of order 10^{-13} cm, in the cosmic superfluidity we are dealing with scales of order millions of light years. We have to embed the Higgs in the curved spacetime of general relativity, and describe how such a quantum field can emerge from the big bang, how it might create all matter in the universe.

To have a qualitative understanding of this theory, one needs to know something about condensed matter physics, quantum field theory, and general relativity. One only needs to know the rudiments of each subject, but it is not easy to find them all in one place, and the purpose of this book is to offer such an option. Whether or not the theory proves to be correct, I hope the reader will find this book interesting, perhaps even amusing.

Kerson Huang
Wakefield, Massachusetts
May, 2016

Acknowledgments

The research reported in this book was carried out between 2011 and 2014 at the Institute of Advanced Studies (IAS), Nanyang Technological University (NTU), Singapore. I wish to thank Professor K. K. Phua (潘国驹) Founding Director of IAS, and Professor Su Guaning (徐冠林), President Emeritus of NTU, for their support, without which this project would not have been possible.

I thank Dr. Xiong Chi (熊持) of IAS for reading the first draft of the manuscript, and offering valuable suggestions.

I thank my editor Lakshmi Narayanan for doing an excellent and expeditious job.

Last but not least, I thank my research team for their contributions:

Good, Michael,
Guo Yulong (郭宇隆),
Liu Xiaopei (刘晓培),
Low Hwee-Boon (刘斐文),
Tung Roh-Suan (童若轩),
Xiong Chi (熊持),
Zhao Xiaofei (赵晓飞).

Contents

Introduction

Physics in the twentieth century was dominated by quantum mechanics and relativity. Their interplay may illuminate the great puzzles of our time: dark energy and dark matter.

Compared with classical mechanics, quantum mechanics has an extra dimension, the quantum phase, which enables systems to enter into a kind of correlation that is impossible to comprehend in classical thinking. When the environment gets complicated, as in the macroscopic world, the phase usually randomizes, and we get classical behavior. Even in the macroscopic world, however, atoms obeying Bose statistics can exhibit bulk quantum effects. When the temperature is sufficiently low, it undergoes the Bose–Einstein phase transition, in which a fraction of the atoms go into the same single-particle state, and become correlated in phase. The variation of the phase in space gives rise to a superfluid velocity.

Spin systems can become phase-correlated, or "entangled", over macroscopic distances, and this is the basis of the technology of quantum information. But that is another story.

We have observed superfluidity in liquid ^{4}He at low temperatures, and manipulated it in cold trapped atomic gases. We have seen vortex activity and quantum turbulence, which is as ubiquitous as classical turbulence. The superconductivity of metals is a form of superfluidity arising from the condensation of paired electrons. We have also discovered that ^{3}He becomes a superfluid below 10^{-3} K, when its fermionic atoms pair up into bosons and condense. Similar condensation of paired fermions also occurs in neutron stars at about 10^6 K. Superfluidity is a well studied subject in diverse systems, both experimentally and in theory.

In particle physics, one introduces the Higgs field, a complex scalar field, in order to generate mass for the vector bosons mediating weak interactions. There is now experimental evidence for this, with the discovery of the associated particle, the Higgs boson. This is a field that can give rise to superfluidity due to the dynamics of its quantum phase. This aspect of the Higgs is not important on the particle-physics scale of 10^{-13} cm, but on the scale of millions of light years, it makes the entire universe a superfluid.

The superfluidity in the interior of a neutron star occurs on an astronomical scale, but it pertains only to stellar structure. We are concerned here with something much bigger. We are talking about an all-pervasive superfluid in the universe. All astrophysical processes take place in this superfluid.

When did this cosmic superfluid appear in the evolution of the universe? One possibility is that it was created at the big bang, before matter existed. We imagine that the superfluid was created in a state of quantum turbulence, and all the matter in the universe was created in this turbulence in a very short time. This will present a new picture of the "inflationary universe".

We have formulated these ideas mathematically, and found that the emergence of the superfluid drives an accelerated expansion of the universe. Thus, one could say that dark energy is the energy density of the cosmic superfluid. When the superfluid density deviates from its equilibrium value, the patches of denser superfluid can be revealed through gravitational lensing, which we then perceive as dark matter. For example, galaxies attract the surrounding superfluid to form dark-matter halos.

In this book, we aim to give a concise introduction to the various fields relevant to our model, and these include condensed matter physics, quantum field theory, and general relativity. We will emphasize physical understanding, and also supply the mathematical background, which should be accessible to advanced undergraduates and graduate students in physics.

Throughout this book, unless otherwise specified, we use units in which $\hbar = c = 1$, and Minkowski metric $\mathrm{diag}(-1, 1, 1, 1)$.

1 Superfluidity and the order parameter

1.1 Bose–Einstein condensation

Bosonic atoms undergo the Bose–Einstein condensation below a critical temperature, in which a fraction of all the atoms go into the same state, forming a condensate with a definite quantum phase. This transition occurs at 2.18 K for liquid helium, and typically around 1 K for cold trapped atoms. As the temperature drops, the condensate fraction increases from zero to 1 at absolute zero. This is illustrated in Fig. 1.1 for liquid ^{4}He. Also shown is the λ-shaped spike in the heat capacity at the transition temperature, which leads to the label "the λ-transition."

As we shall see, the condensate is called a "superfluid", for its apparent lack of viscosity. At finite temperatures those atoms not in the condensate behave like a "normal" fluid, and the system can be described by a "two-fluid model", in which the superfluid and the normal fluid are two interpenetrating fluids with the properties

$$\rho = \rho_s + \rho_n$$
$$\mathbf{j} = \mathbf{j}_s + \mathbf{j}_n$$

(1.1)

where ρ and $\mathbf{j}$ designate density and current density, respectively,

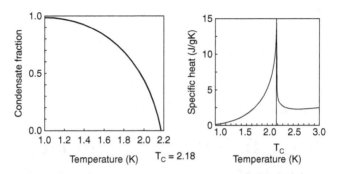

Fig. 1.1 (Left) Condensate fraction of liquid ^{4}He as function of temperature. (Right) The specific heat shows a λ-shaped spike at the transition temperature $T_c = 2.18$ K. This gives rise to the label "λ-transition".

with the conservation law

$$\frac{\partial \rho}{\partial t} + \nabla \cdot \mathbf{j} = 0 \tag{1.2}$$

Landau [1] identified the normal fluid at low temperatures as a gas of phonons excited from the condensate. A two-fluid hydrodynamics has been developed and described by Khalatnikov [2].

In cold trapped atomic gases, one can create and manipulate the condensate under controlled conditions. Figure 1.2(a) shows a condensate falling under gravity when released from the trap. Figure 1.2(b) shows interference fringes between two overlapping condensates, demonstrating that the condensate is a macroscopic quantum state with a definite phase. The condensation is due to Bose symmetry, not interparticle interactions, and it happens even for an ideal Bose gas; but interparticle interaction, no matter how weak, is necessary, to lock the quantum phases of the atoms together.

The condensate is a "superfluid", in that it can flow through pipes frictionless at low velocities, or that an object can move through the fluid with no friction at low relative velocities. However, it is not a non-viscous classical fluid. The absence of dissipation is a quantum mechanical effect arising from the paucity

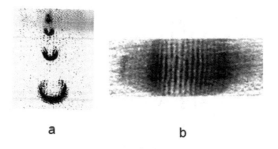

a   b

Fig. 1.2 (Left) Bose–Einsten condensate of sodium atoms falls freely under gravity. (Right) Interference fringes between two overlapping condensates show that each has a definite quantum phase. (MIT experiments, courtesy W. Ketterle)

of excited states, on account of Bose symmetry. In fact, the low-energy excitations are solely phonons (sound waves), with energy-momentum relation $\varepsilon = c|\mathbf{p}|$, where c is the sound velocity. Suppose an object moves through the fluid with velocity $\mathbf{v}_{ext}$. At absolute zero, it can excite the fluid only by creating phonons, transferring energy ΔE and momentum $\Delta \mathbf{P}$:

$$\Delta E = c \sum_i |\mathbf{p}_i|$$
$$\Delta \mathbf{P} = \sum_i \mathbf{p}_i \tag{1.3}$$

Thus

$$|\Delta \mathbf{P}| \leq \sum_i |\mathbf{p}_i| = \Delta E / c$$

On the other hand, we must have

$$\Delta E = \mathbf{v}_{ext} \cdot \Delta \mathbf{P} \tag{1.4}$$

Thus $\Delta E \leq v_{ext}|\Delta \mathbf{P}|$, and this leads to

$$v_{ext} \leq c \tag{1.5}$$

That is, the object can move without friction as long as its velocity is less than the sound velocity. At finite temperatures, the object can scatter the phonons already present, and the critical velocity is lowered.

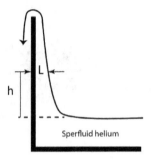

Fig. 1.3 Superfluid helium can climb over the wall of its container, because it coats the wall with a thick film maintained by quantum pressure. An estimate gives $L \propto 1/\sqrt{h}$.

A startling behavior of superfluid helium is that it can climb over the wall of its container. This is because it coats the wall with a thick film that is maintained by quantum pressure, as illustrated in Fig. 1.3. Consider a fluid element of the film of volume ΔV at height h above the surface. The energy of the element is dominated by gravity and quantum kinetic energy, which amounts to $\hbar^2/2mL^2$ per particle:

$$E_{\text{grav}} = \rho g h \Delta V$$

$$E_{\text{kin}} = \frac{\hbar^2}{2mL^2} \frac{f\rho}{m} \Delta V$$

(1.6)

where ρ is the mass density, L the thickness of the film, and f the fraction of atoms in the condensate. Writing $\Delta V = kL$, and minimizing the total energy with respect to L, we obtain

$$L = \frac{L_0}{\sqrt{h}}$$

(1.7)

where $L_0 = (\hbar/m)\sqrt{f/2g}$.

1.2 The order parameter

Landau [3] proposed a general phenomenological theory of phase transitions, based on the idea that the system changes from a less "ordered" state to a more ordered one, or vice versa. The precise meaning of "order" depends on the system, but the general idea of a change in order applies to all. One can quantify the amount of order present by an "order parameter", which is a complex field in the case of Bose–Einstein condensation, because the "order" pertains to a phase angle. It satisfies a nonlinear Schrödinger equation (NLSE) known as the Gross–Pitaevskii (GP) equation [4]:

$$-\frac{\hbar^2}{2m}\psi + (g\psi^*\psi - \mu_0)\psi = i\hbar\frac{\partial\psi}{\partial t} \tag{1.8}$$

where m is the atomic mass, μ_0 the chemical potential, and

$$g = \frac{4\pi a\hbar}{m} \tag{1.9}$$

is a low-energy interaction parameter, in which a is the S-wave scattering length between atoms.

In a phase representation

$$\psi = \sqrt{\rho}e^{i\varphi} \tag{1.10}$$

we identify ρ as the superfluid density, which in the absence of external potential is given by $\rho_0 = \mu_0/g$. The superfluid velocity is given by

$$\mathbf{v}_s = \frac{\hbar}{m}\nabla\varphi \tag{1.11}$$

The real and imaginary parts of the GP equation lead to the hydrodynamic equations:

$$\frac{\partial\rho}{\partial t} + \nabla\cdot(\rho\mathbf{v}_s) = 0$$

$$m\left(\frac{\partial}{\partial t} + \mathbf{v}_s\cdot\nabla\right)\mathbf{v}_s = \nabla\left(\mu_0 - g\rho + \frac{\hbar^2}{2m}\frac{1}{\sqrt{\rho}}\nabla^2\sqrt{\rho}\right) \tag{1.12}$$

The first equation is the continuity equation. The second is the analog of Euler's equation. The last term in the brackets on the right-hand side is the quantum pressure.

1.3 Spontaneous symmetry breaking

The GP equation can be derived from quantum field theory. Let $\hat{\Psi}(x,t)$ be the quantum operator, whose action on a quantum state of the system is to annihilate an atom at position x at time t. The Hamiltonian is given by

$$H = \int d^3x \left(\frac{\hbar^2}{2m}\nabla\hat{\Psi}^\dagger \cdot \nabla\hat{\Psi} + u_{\text{ext}}\hat{\Psi}^\dagger\hat{\Psi} \right)$$

$$+ \frac{1}{2}\int d^3x d^3y \hat{\Psi}^\dagger(x)\hat{\Psi}^\dagger(y)u(x-y)\hat{\Psi}(y)\hat{\Psi}(x) \quad (1.13)$$

where an overhead caret $\wedge$ denotes quantum field operator, $u_{\text{ext}}(x)$ is the potential of an external trap, and $u(x-y)$ the interparticle interaction potential. The condensate corresponds to a non-vanishing expectation of the field operator, and the order parameter is the "condensate wave function" defined as the expectation value of the field operator:

$$\psi = \langle\hat{\Psi}\rangle \quad (1.14)$$

We can loosely think of it as the wave function of an atom in the condensate. We write

$$\hat{\Psi} = \psi + \hat{\eta} \quad (1.15)$$

Substituting this into (1.13), using the low-energy approximation $u(x-y) = g\delta^3(x-y)$, and neglecting $\hat{\eta}$, we obtain a mean-field Hamiltonian:

$$H_1 = \int d^3x \left[\frac{\hbar^2}{2m}\nabla\psi^\dagger \cdot \nabla\psi + u_{\text{ext}}\psi^\dagger\psi + V\left(\psi^\dagger\psi\right) \right] \quad (1.16)$$

where $V(\psi^\dagger\psi)$ is a field potential:

$$V\left(\psi^\dagger\psi\right) = \frac{g}{2}\left(\psi^\dagger\psi\right)^2 - \mu_0\psi^\dagger\psi \quad (1.17)$$

where we have added the term $-\mu_0\hat{\Psi}^\dagger\hat{\Psi}$ to shift the zero point of energy. For $u_{\text{ext}} = 0$, we have a uniform ground state in which

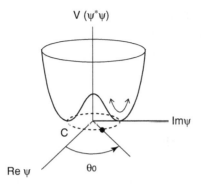

Fig. 1.4 The "wine-bottle" potential leads to spontaneous symmetry breaking. The black dot indicates the ground state, chosen out of any equivalent point around the circle C, thus picking out a definite phase angle θ_0. Small oscillations on the circle C about the ground state correspond to the Goldstone mode or phonons. Motion indicated by the arc with arrows corresponds to the excitation of an atom.

$\psi = \sqrt{\mu_0/g}$. The time evolution of ψ is generated by H_1, leading to the GP equation.

The Hamiltonian H_1 is invariant under the global gauge transformation $\psi \rightarrow e^{i\theta}\psi$, where θ is a real constant, and the transformations form a group $U(1)$. As illustrated in Fig. 1.4, the minima of V lie on the circle C, any point of which can be a ground state, but the system must choose one of them. This singles out a definite phase θ_0 and breaks the $U(1)$ symmetry. This phenomenon, in which the ground state does not have the symmetry of the Hamiltonian, is called "spontaneous symmetry breaking" [5]. The symmetry is not lost, being re-expressed through the fact that there are an infinite number of equivalent ground states that transform into each other under $U(1)$. Motions along the circle C in Fig. 1.4 correspond to Goldstone modes, or phonons. Motion along the arrowed curve corresponds to the excitation of an atom.

The order parameter is a phenomenological way to express spontaneous symmetry breaking, but how does it really come about physically? Basically, it happens because the system gets stuck in a pocket in phase space, in its time evolution. For example, ferro-magnetism occurs because, when a block of spin of size N becomes aligned, it takes time of the order of e^N for the whole block to flip due to thermal fluctuations; for macroscopic N the time is vastly greater than the age of the universe.

1.4   Quantized vorticity

The condensate wave function ψ must be a continuous function in space, and hence its phase must be continuous modulo 2π. The circulation, defined by the following line integral, is therefore quantized:

$$\oint_C dx \cdot v_s = \frac{\hbar}{m} \oint_C dx \cdot \nabla\varphi = \frac{2\pi\hbar n}{m} \quad (n = 0, \pm 1, \pm 2, \ldots) \quad (1.18)$$

where C is a closed loop in space. For $n \neq 0$, the loop cannot be shrunken to zero continuously, and C must encircle a vortex line, on which $\psi = 0$, as illustrated in Fig. 1.5. In practice, we need to only consider a single quantum $n = \pm 1$, because from energy considerations, multiple quanta will break up into single ones.

The vortex line cannot terminate inside the fluid. It must either form a closed loop, or terminate on a boundary of the fluid. The superfluid density vanishes on the vortex line. Away from the vortex

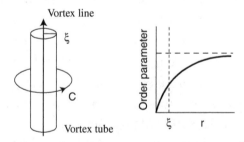

Fig. 1.5   The vortex tube. The superfluid density vanishes on the central vortex line, with "healing length" ζ. The superfluid velocity decreases inversely with distance from the central vortex line.

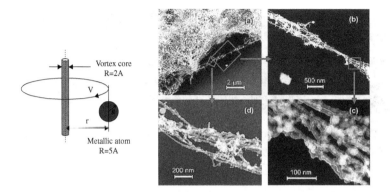

Fig. 1.6   Vortex lines in superfluid helium made visible by fine metallic powder sticking to vortex tube surfaces due to Bernoulli pressure. From [4].

line, it rises to an asymptotic value with a "healing length" ζ as illustrated in Fig. 1.5. Thus, the vortex line is effectively a vortex tube of radius ζ. The GP equation (1.8) gives, in the absence of external potential,

$$\zeta = \frac{\sqrt{g}}{\mu_0} \qquad (1.19)$$

For a circular loop C of very small radius r in Fig. 1.5, we can treat the local vortex line as a segment of a straight line. Symmetry then dictates that $\mathbf{v}$ be tangential to the circle C, with constant magnitude $v = 2\pi\hbar n/mr$. The $1/r$ behavior creates a Bernoulli pressure, and impurities will tend to stick to the vortex tube. Vortex lines in superfluid helium have been made visible through this effect, by sprinkling metallic powder into the liquid, as shown in Fig. 1.6 [6].

In superfluid helium and cold condensed atomic gases, vortices can be created by rotating the container. When the angular velocity of the container exceeds a critical value, the superfluid responds by developing vortex lines parallel to the axis of rotation [7, 8]. Experimental results in a trapped atomic gas are shown in Fig. 1.7, showing the development of a vortex lattice as the angular frequency increases [7]. In the limit of very high angular frequency, this makes the superfluid rotate like a rigid body.

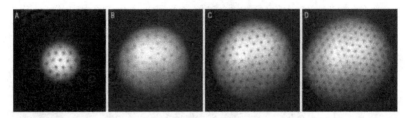

Fig. 1.7   A Bose–Einstein condensate in a rotating container develops vortex lattices of increasing size as the angular frequency increases. From [7].

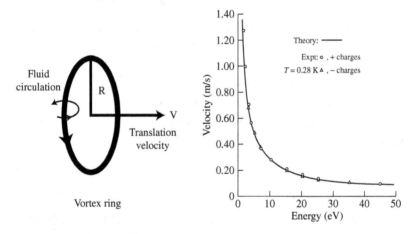

Fig. 1.8   A vortex ring of radius R has translational velocity $v \sim R^{-1} \ln R$ and energy $E \sim R \ln R$. The right panel is the result from an experiment in which charged particles are shot into superfluid helium to create and be trapped by vortex rings [10].

The simplest closed vortex line is a vortex ring in the shape of a circle of radius R. It moves normal to the plane of the circle, with velocity $v \sim R^{-1} \ln R$, and energy $E \sim R \ln R$. Thus, roughly speaking, $E \sim v^{-1}$. By shooting alpha particles or electrons into superfluid helium, vortex rings can be created, which trap the projectiles [8] to form charged vortex rings. The velocity-energy curve of such composite objects can be obtained by dragging them across the liquid against an electric field. The results fit that of quantized vortex rings with unit quantum, as shown in Fig. 1.8.

1.5 Superconductivity

Superconductivity [11] may be thought as superfluidity arising from a condensation of bound electron pairs, the Cooper pairs. They have charge $q = 2e$, and the Hamiltonian generalizes from (1.13) to

$$H_2 = \int d^3x \left[\frac{\hbar^2}{2m} \left(\nabla + \frac{i\hbar q}{c}\mathbf{A} \right) \psi^\dagger \cdot \left(\nabla - \frac{i\hbar q}{c}\mathbf{A} \right) \psi + V \left(\psi^\dagger \psi \right) \right]$$

(1.20)

where we have omitted the external potential u_{ext}. This leads to the Ginzburg–Landau (GL) equation for the order parameter [12]:

$$-\frac{\hbar^2}{2m} \left(\nabla - \frac{i\hbar q}{c}\mathbf{A} \right)^2 \psi + (g\psi^*\psi - \mu_0)\psi = i\hbar \frac{\partial \psi}{\partial t}$$

(1.21)

where A is a magnetic field, and g is a model parameter. The superconductor is thus characterized by a phase angle, that of ψ. When two superconductors touch each other, the difference in their phases induces a supercurrent to flow from one body to the other, and this is known as the Josephson effect.

A conserved current of the system is

$$\mathbf{J} = \frac{\hbar q}{2mi} (\psi \nabla \psi^* - \psi^* \nabla \psi) - \frac{q^2}{mc}\psi^*\psi\mathbf{A}$$

(1.22)

Using this in Maxwell's equation $\nabla \times \nabla \times \mathbf{A} = \frac{4\pi}{c}\mathbf{J}$, we obtain, in an appropriate gauge,

$$\left(\nabla^2 + \frac{4\pi n q^2}{mc^2} \right) \mathbf{A} = 0$$

(1.23)

where $n = \psi^*\psi$. This says that an external magnetic field can penetrate into the interior of the superconductor only to a depth of

$$d = \sqrt{\frac{mc^2}{4\pi n q^2}}$$

(1.24)

This is known as the Meissner effect. We can also say the superconducting body is a medium in which the photon has mass

$$m_{photon} = \frac{\hbar}{cd}$$

(1.25)

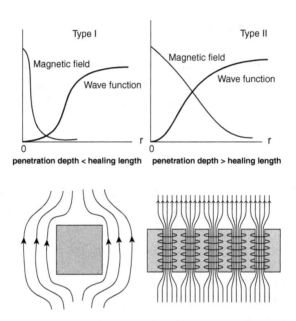

Fig. 1.9   Upper panels show the behavior of the magnetic field and condensate wave function near the surface ($r = 0$) of the superconductor. Lower panels illustrate the expulsion of magnet flux in Type I superconductors, and the formation of a quantized-flux lattice in Type II case.

The existence of two length scales, the healing length ζ and the penetration length d, leads to two types of superconductor:

Type I $(\zeta > d)$ Magnetic field completely expelled from interior
Type II $(\zeta < d)$ Magnetic field that penetrates the body in
                          quantized vortex tubes

The vortex tubes carry quantized magnetic flux in units of hc/e, and have an effective radius of the order of ζ. We can understand such behavior by referring to Fig. 1.9, which depicts the magnetic field and the condensate wave function near the surface of the superconductor. In Type I case, there is little overlap between magnetic field and wave function. If a flux tube were formed, the system can lower the energy by expelling it outside, and filling the hole in the order parameter. For Type II, an overlap between magnetic field and order parameter lowers the energy, creating a negative surface tension. Thus, flux tubes are formed, maintained by solenoidal supercurrents.

1.6 Higgs mechanism

We recall that the Hamiltonian H_1 has global gauge invariance, which is spontaneously broken by the definite phase of the order parameter. As a result, there are Goldstone modes, which are phonons. The Hamiltonian H_2 for a superconductor has a higher symmetry, owing to the gauge coupling to the electromagnetic field, in which one makes the replacement

$$\nabla \psi \to \left(\nabla - \frac{i\hbar q}{c} \mathbf{A} \right) \psi$$

The Hamiltonian is now invariant under a local gauge transformation:

$$\psi \to \exp(i\chi)\psi$$
$$\mathbf{A} \to \mathbf{A} + \frac{c}{\hbar q} \nabla \chi \tag{1.26}$$

where $\chi(x,t)$ is an arbitrary function.

The existence of a definite phase of the order parameter spontaneously breaks the local gauge invariance. As a consequence, the gauge field becomes massive, and the Goldstone mode becomes the longitudinal degree of freedom of the massive gauge field. This effect was embodied in the GL equation a long time ago, but was independently discovered in particle theory, where it was called the "Higgs mechanism".

References

[1] L. D. Landau, *J. Phys. USSR* **5**, 71 (1941).
[2] I. M. Khalatnikov, *An Introduction to the Theory of Superfluidity* (W. A. Benjamin, New York, 1965).

[3] L. D. Landau, *Phys. Z. Sowjetunion* **11**, 26 (1937).

[4] F. Dalfovo, S. Giorgini, L. P. Pitaevskii, A. Stringari, *Rev. Mod. Phys.* **71**, 463 (1999).

[5] K. Huang, *Quarks, Leptons, and Gauge Fields*, 2nd ed. (World Scientific, Singapore, 1992).

[6] V. Lebedev, P. Moroshkin, B. Grobety, E. Gordon, A. Weis, *J. Low Temp. Phys.* **165**, 166 (2011).

[7] R. J. Donelly, *Quantized Vortices in Helium II* (Cambridge University Press, Cambridge, England, 1991).

[8] A. L. Fetter, *Rev. Mod. Phys.* **81**, 647 (2009).

[9] Abo-Shaeer, I. Raman, W. Ketterle, *Phys. Rev. Lett.* **88**, 070409 (2002).

[10] G. W. Rayfield and F. Reif, *Phys. Rev.* **136**, A1194 (1964).

[11] P. G. DeGennes, *Superconductivity of Metals and Alloys* (Westview Press, Boulder, 1999).

[12] V. L. Ginzburg and L. D. Landau, *Zh. Eksp. Teor. Fiz.* **20**, 1064 (1950).

2 Quantum turbulence

2.1 Vortex dynamics

A superfluid is accompanied by a normal fluid at finite temperatures, which exhibits classical turbulence, in which vorticity plays an important role. Through "vortex stretching", energy cascades from a larger length scale to a smaller one, and finally dissipates at the molecular level. This energy cascade leads to the Kolmogorov energy spectrum $E \sim k^{-5/3}$, where k is the wave number.

The superfluid also exhibits turbulence, but there is no vortex stretching, because vorticity is quantized. Instead, energy cascade proceeds through vortex reconnections, in which a large vortex ring degrades into smaller ones, and the small rings further degrade into still smaller ones, resulting in a "vortex tangle" that is quantum turbulence. There are important differences with classical turbulence. While the velocity distribution in classical turbulence is Gaussian, that in quantum turbulence has a power law tail, due to the fact that the reconnection process creates high-velocity jets in the superfluid. To understand quantum turbulence, we must start with a discussion of the dynamics of quantum vorticity.

A vortex configuration is characterized by a vortex line, a directed space curve on which the superfluid density vanishes. It

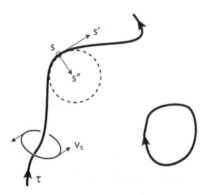

Fig. 2.1 The vortex configuration is specified by the vortex line, on which the superfluid density vanishes. The superfluid velocity flows around the line, defining a sense via the right-hand rule. The vortex line can only end at a boundary, or upon itself, in which case it is a vortex ring. Let **s** be the vector position at a point on the string, and let the distance along the string be τ. Thus, $\mathbf{s}' = d\mathbf{s}/d\tau$ is tangent to the string, and $\mathbf{s}''$ is normal to the string. The tangential circle, shown dotted, has normal proportional to $\mathbf{s}' \times \mathbf{s}''$, and radius $|\mathbf{s}''|^{-1}$.

can be described by a position vector $\mathbf{s}(\tau, t)$, where τ is a parameter that runs along the line, and t is the time. The vortex line may be made up of disjoint closed loops, and curves that terminate on boundaries. The parameter τ runs through all of the components according to some convention. The superfluid density vanishes on the vortex line with a characteristic healing length ζ. We can picture the vortex line as a tube with effective radius ζ. This "core size" is supposed to be much smaller than any other length in the theory. When we refer to a point on the vortex line, we mean some point within the core.

Let us denote

$$\mathbf{s}' = \frac{\partial \mathbf{s}}{\partial \tau}$$

$$\dot{\mathbf{s}} = \frac{\partial \mathbf{s}}{\partial t}$$

(2.1)

The vector $\mathbf{s}'$ is tangent to the vortex line, and $\mathbf{s}''$ is normal to it, as depicted in Fig. 2.1. The local radius of curvature is given by

$R = |\mathbf{s}''|^{-1}$. We recall from (1.18) that

$$\oint_C d\mathbf{x} \cdot \mathbf{v}_s = \frac{2\pi\hbar n}{m} \tag{2.2}$$

Using Stokes' theorem, we can rewrite this in the form

$$\nabla \times \mathbf{v}_0 = \kappa \tag{2.3}$$

where $\kappa(\mathbf{r}, t)$, the vorticity density, is non-vanishing only on the vortex line:

$$\kappa(\mathbf{r}, t) = \kappa_0 \int d\tau \, \delta\left(\mathbf{r} - \mathbf{s}(\tau, t)\right) \tag{2.4}$$

We can have $\nabla \times \mathbf{v}_s \neq 0$ even though $v \propto \nabla\varphi$, because the phase φ is not continuous. Another way to see this is that closed loops around the vortex line cannot be shrunken to zero continuously, making the space non-simply connected.

We can decompose the superfluid velocity into an irrotational part $\mathbf{v}_0$, and a rotational part $\mathbf{b}$:

$$\begin{aligned}
\mathbf{v}_s &= \mathbf{v}_0 + \mathbf{b} \\
\nabla \times \mathbf{v}_0 &= \nabla \cdot \mathbf{b} = 0 \\
\nabla \times \mathbf{b} &= \kappa
\end{aligned} \tag{2.5}$$

The velocity field $\mathbf{b}$ is like a magnetic field produced by the current density κ, and is given by the Biot–Savart law

$$\mathbf{b}(\mathbf{r}, t) = \frac{\kappa_0}{4\pi} \int \frac{(\mathbf{s}_1 - \mathbf{r}) \times d\mathbf{s}_1}{|\mathbf{s}_1 - r|^3} \tag{2.6}$$

where $\mathbf{s}_1$ is a particular point on the vortex line, and the integral extends over all $\mathbf{s}_1$.

The velocity at any point $\mathbf{r}$ depends on the shape of the entire vortex line. For $\mathbf{r}$ on the vortex line itself, one can make a "local approximation", which takes into account only influences coming from the immediate neighborhood of $\mathbf{r}$, resulting in the following picture. The vortex line at any point has a local radius of curvature R. A vortex ring of radius R tangent to the vortex line at that point

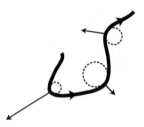

Fig. 2.2   The velocity of the vortex line at any point is approximately the translational velocity of the tangential vortex ring at that point. It is normal to the ring,
with magnitude inversely proportional to the radius of the ring, which is the local radius of curvature of the vortex line. Thus, the sharper the vortex bends, the
faster it moves at that point.

would move normal to the ring with velocity $v \propto R^{-1} \ln R$. This is
taken to be the local velocity of the vortex line. Thus, a vortex line
generally executes a self-induced writhing motion, as illustrated in
Fig. 2.2, and described by Schwarz's equation [1]

$$\dot{\mathbf{s}} = \mathbf{v}_s + \beta \mathbf{s}' \times \mathbf{s}'' \tag{2.7}$$

where

$$\beta = \frac{\kappa_0}{4\pi} \ln \left(\frac{c_0 \bar{R}}{\zeta} \right) \tag{2.8}$$

where $\bar{R}$ is the average radius of curvature, and c_0 is a constant of
order unity.

Refinements include the following effects. We see from (2.7), the
local velocity of the vortex line $\dot{\mathbf{s}}(\tau, t) \equiv \mathbf{v}_L(\tau, t)$, in general does not
coincide with the local superfluid velocity $\mathbf{v}_s(\mathbf{s}(\tau, t), t) \equiv \mathbf{v}_{sl}(\tau, t)$,
and the vortex line experiences a Magnus force per unit length f_M:

$$\frac{\mathbf{f}_M}{\rho_s \kappa_0} = \frac{\mathbf{s}'}{|\mathbf{s}'|} \times (\mathbf{v}_L - \mathbf{v}_{sl}) \tag{2.9}$$

At finite temperatures, the vortex line faces a normal fluid "wind"
with velocity $\mathbf{v}_n$, and there is a frictional force per unit length $\mathbf{f}_D$ on
the vortex line:

$$\frac{\mathbf{f}_D}{\rho_s \kappa_0} = -\alpha \mathbf{s}' \times [\mathbf{s}' \times (\mathbf{v}_{ns} - \beta \mathbf{s}' \times \mathbf{s}'') - \alpha' \mathbf{s}' \times (\mathbf{v}_{ns} - \beta \mathbf{s}' \times \mathbf{s}'')]$$

$$\tag{2.10}$$

where $\mathbf{v}_{ns} = \mathbf{v}_n - \mathbf{v}$, and α, α' are temperature-dependent parameters.

We must emphasize that the GP equation fully describes superfluid hydrodynamics, including vorticity. While the discussion above gives a physical picture of the motion of the vortex line, to obtain quantitative results, it is more accurate and efficient to numerically solve the GP equation.

2.2 Vortex reconnections

Feynman [2] suggested that when two vortex lines cross, they would reconnect, and that through this process, vortex loops would degrade into smaller loops, eventually reaching a state he dubbed "quantum turbulence". His original sketch of the process is shown on the upper panel of Fig. 2.3. The lower panel shows actual photographs of a vortex-reconnection event in superfluid helium [3].

Figure 2.4(a) shows the configurations of two vortex lines before and after their reconnection, with a cusp on each of the subsequent lines. Since the local velocity of a vortex line is inversely proportional to the local radius of curvature, the near-zero radii of the cusps make them rapidly spring away from each other, creating two jets of energy in the background superfluid. This is a mechanism that can convert potential energy into kinetic energy in a short time. Figure 2.4(b) shows the similar process of the reconnection of magnetic flux lines in the sun, which is responsible for the creation of solar flares [4].

Schwarz [1] estimated that two vortex line segments of approximately the same curvature R reconnect when they are within a critical distance

$$\delta \approx 2R \ln \frac{R}{c_0 R_0} \qquad (2.11)$$

where c_0 and R_0 are constants. When the lines approach each other, they reorient themselves into an antiparallel configuration, if

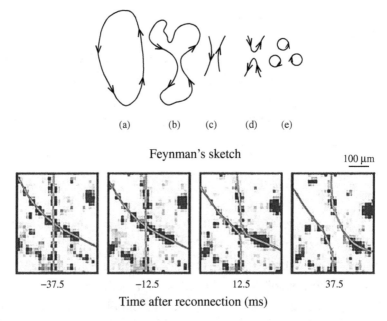

Fig. 2.3   (Upper panel) Feynman's sketch of the decay of a vortex ring into smaller ones through repeated reconnections, eventually leading to a state of quantum turbulence [2]. (Lower panel) Actual photographs of a reconnection event in superfluid helium [3].

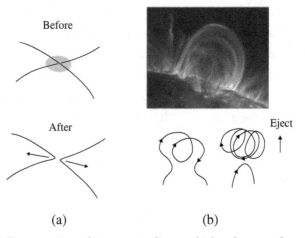

Fig. 2.4   (a) Reconnection of two vortex lines, which subsequently spring away from each other at high speed, creating two jets of energy. (b) Magnetic reconnections in the Sun produce solar flares [4].

necessary, before reconnecting. Since the local velocity of a vortex line is approximately that of the tangential vortex ring $v \sim R^{-1} \ln R$, we have

$$\delta \sim v^{-1} \tag{2.12}$$

The reconnection process has been studied numerically using the GP equation [5], and using Schwarz's equations [6].

2.3 The vortex tangle: quantum turbulence

Schwarz [1] created a vortex tangle via computer simulation, by exposing a vortex ring to "head wind", i.e. heat flows counter to the ring's translational motion. The vortex ring slows down and expands. In a tail wind, on the other hand, it will speed up and shrink. Thus, vortex rings in a head wind are subject to two opposing effects: growth due to head wind, and degradation due to reconnections. A balance between these two tendencies creates a steady-state vortex tangle, which is quantum turbulence.

An external heat current is necessary for the maintenance of quantum turbulence, just as input airflow in a wind tunnel maintains classical turbulence. When the heat current stops, the vortex tangle will decay into ever smaller vortex rings, and eventually disappear into the sea of thermal fluctuations.

Figure 2.5 shows Schwarz's simulation, which details the formation of quantum turbulence due to reconnections [1]. The fractal dimension of a vortex tangle similar to that in the last frame is 1.62 [6].

The quantum turbulence has similarities with, and differences from, classical turbulence. Experiments in superfluid helium [8], and computer simulations of the GP equation [9] reveal that both has the Kolmogorov energy spectrum $E(k) \sim k^{-5/3}$, as shown in Fig. 2.6. This can be explained by the fact that, both classical and quantum turbulence can be described by vortex lines that do not

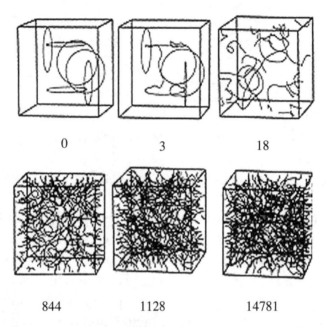

Fig. 2.5   Computer simulation of the formation of vortex tangle (quantum turbulence) [1]. The number of vortex reconnections is given under each time frame. The fractal of dimension *a* of vortex tangle similar to that in the last frame is 1.62 [6].

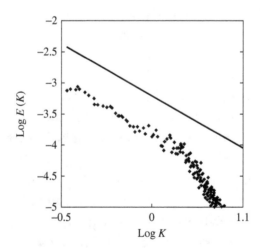

Fig. 2.6   Energy spectrum $E(k)$ of quantum turbulence, where k is the wave number, as computed from the GP equation, follows Kolmogorov's law $E(k) \sim k^{-5/3}$, which corresponds to the straight-line. From [9].

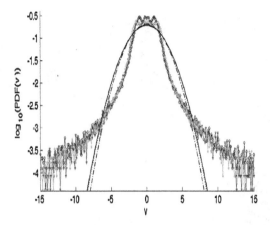

Fig. 2.7 Velocity distribution in quantum turbulence in superfluid helium. It deviates from the Gaussian distribution of classical turbulence in that it has a power-law tail coming from vortex reconnections. From [11].

cross themselves, because of Kelvin's theorem in the classical case, and reconnections in the quantum case. As far as the power spectrum is concerned, such vortex line belongs to the universal class of random self-avoiding walk (SAW), which features an exponent of 5/3, and also applies to a polymer chain [10].

On the other hand, experiments in superfluid helium reveal that the velocity distribution in quantum turbulence is different from the Gaussian distribution in classical turbulence, in that it has a power-law tail, as shown in Fig. 2.7 [11]. This is due to the fact that quantum turbulence is maintained by reconnections, which creates high-velocity jets.

We can estimate the average superfluid speed v in a vortex tangle as follows. Let ℓ be the density of vortex lines, i.e. the number of vortex lines per unit volume. In a sufficiently small volume element, the lines must be parallel to each other, or else they would reconnect. Consider a volume element in the shape of a thin square wafer, with the vortex lines normal to the surface of the wafer, with average spacing δ between the vortex lines. We can see that $\ell \sim \delta^2$. On the

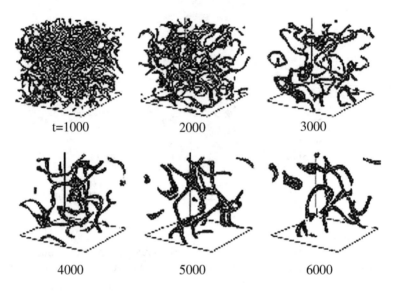

t=1000   2000   3000

4000   5000   6000

Fig. 2.8 Computer simulation of a Bose–Einstein condensate created far from equilibrium. It goes through a period of quantum turbulence before settling into thermal equilibrium. From [12].

other hand, $\delta \sim v^{-1}$ from (2.12). Thus

$$v \sim \sqrt{\ell} \tag{2.13}$$

We expect quantum turbulence to occur when a condensate was created far from thermal equilibrium, and the equilibrium was reached only after the turbulence decayed. This is like pouring water into a glass to create classical turbulence, and is verified via computer simulation [12], as shown in Fig. 2.8.

2.4 Vinen's equation

The vortex tangle in quantum turbulence is the result of balancing the growth rate of new vortex loops due to external heating, against the rate of degradation due to reconnections. These two phenomena have their own scaling behavior, which are expressed in Vinen's equation [13]

$$\frac{d\ell}{dt} = A\ell^{3/2} - B\ell^2 \tag{2.14}$$

where $\ell(t)$ is the vortex line density (average length per unit volume), and A and B are temperature-dependent parameters. The first term gives the growth rate, and the second term is the decay rate. Originally proposed as a phenomenological equation, it has been derived from vortex dynamics by Schwarz [1], and experimentally verified in superfluid helium [14].

2.5 String theory of relativistic quantized vorticity

Quantized vorticity corresponds to a singular solution of the NLSE in which the field vanishes on a vortex line, as discussed earlier in Chapter 1. It is useful to have a physical understanding to identify the variables pertinent to these solutions, as we have done in Sec. 2.1. Here, we want to generalize the variables to the relativistic case, and reformulate the action in terms of them. In the relativistic domain, the order parameter is a relativistic scalar field $\phi(x)$ governed by the Lagrangian density

$$\mathcal{L} = \partial^\mu \phi^* \partial_\mu \phi - V(\phi^* \phi) \tag{2.15}$$

and the equation of motion is NLKG (nonlinear Klein–Gordon equation):

$$\left(\nabla^2 - \frac{\partial^2}{\partial t^2} - V' \right) \phi = 0 \tag{2.16}$$

where $V' = dV/d(\phi^* \phi)$. The vortex line is a space curve that sweeps out a world sheet in 4D spacetime. The dynamics of the vortex line is therefore that of a relativistic string, which has been widely discussed in the literature [15, 16]. We summarize very briefly how to pass from field theory describing the order parameter to string theory describing relativistic vorticity, omitting derivations.

In the phase representation, we write

$$\phi = Fe^{i\sigma} \tag{2.17}$$

The superfluid velocity is proportional to $\nabla\sigma$. (This will be discussed in more detail in Sec. 3.4.) It is convenient to work with the 4-vector

$$v^\mu \equiv \partial^\mu\sigma \tag{2.18}$$

The quantization condition is a property of v^μ:

$$\oint_C d\mathbf{x}\cdot\mathbf{v} = 2\pi n \quad (n = 0, \pm1, \pm2, \ldots) \tag{2.19}$$

To begin, we covariantly separate potential (irrotational) flow and vorticity by writing [17]

$$v^\mu = \partial^\mu\chi + b^\mu \tag{2.20}$$

where χ is a continuous function (whereas σ is only continuous modulo 2π), and b^μ describes vorticity. We define a "smooth" order parameter ψ, with the phase χ:

$$\psi = Fe^{i\chi} \tag{2.21}$$

The Lagrangian density can be rewritten in terms of ψ and b^μ as

$$\begin{aligned} \mathcal{L}_0 &= \partial^\mu\phi^*\partial_\mu\phi - V(\phi^*\phi) \\ &= \left(\partial^\mu + ib^\mu\right)\psi^*\left(\partial_\mu - ib_\mu\right)\psi - V(\psi^*\psi) \end{aligned} \tag{2.22}$$

This implies that we can start with potential flow described by ψ, and introduce vorticity by introducing a gauge field b^μ. The Lagrangian density is invariant under a local gauge transformation $\psi \to \psi'$, $b_\mu \to b'_\mu$, with

$$\begin{aligned} \psi' &= e^{-i\alpha}\psi \\ b'_\mu &= b_\mu + \partial_\mu\alpha \end{aligned} \tag{2.23}$$

where $\alpha(x)$ is a continuous function; the transformation is equivalent to a shift $\chi \to \chi - \alpha$. Note that **b** has a dual personality: on the one hand, it is like a magnetic field according to the Biot–Savart law (2.6), and on the other hand, it is a gauge field in the present context.

The vortex quantization condition refers to b^μ only, and may be represented covariantly as

$$\oint_C dx \cdot \mathbf{b} = \oint_C dx^\mu b_\mu = 2\pi n \quad (n = 0, \pm 1, 2, \dots) \qquad (2.24)$$

By means of the Stokes theorem, we can rewrite the above as

$$\frac{1}{2} \int_S dS^{\mu\nu} b_{\mu\nu} = 2\pi n \quad (n = 0, \pm 1, 2, \dots) \qquad (2.25)$$

where S is a surface bounded by the closed path C, $dS^{\mu\nu}$ is a surface element, and $b^{\mu\nu}$ is the antisymmetric vorticity tensor

$$b^{\mu\nu} \equiv (\partial^\mu \partial^\nu - \partial^\nu \partial^\mu)\,\sigma \qquad (2.26)$$

which clearly shows that vorticity arises from a discontinuity in the phase σ. This tensor is non-vanishing only on the vortex line. The covariant generalization of the vorticity $\kappa = \nabla \times \mathbf{b}$ is

$$K^\mu = \epsilon^{\mu\nu\rho\tau} b_\nu \partial_\rho b_\tau \qquad (2.27)$$

The spatial components give $K^i = \epsilon^{i0jk} b_0 \partial_j b_k$, and thus $\kappa^i = K^i/b_0$. Since $\mathbf{b}$ is like a magnetic field, with $\nabla \cdot \mathbf{b} = 0$, we can introduce the vector potential through $\mathbf{b} = \nabla \times \mathbf{A}$. The covariant generalization of this is [18]

$$b_\mu = \frac{1}{2}\epsilon_{\mu\nu\lambda\rho}\partial^\nu B^{\lambda\rho} \qquad (2.28)$$

where the generalized potential is the antisymmetric tensor $B^{\lambda\rho}$. It is determined only up to gauge transformations, and one can impose the "Lorentz gauge" $\partial_\mu B^{\mu\nu} = 0$ plus $B^{k0} = 0$ [19] to reduce the number of independent components of $B^{\mu\nu}$ to one. The field strength tensor corresponding to $B^{\mu\nu}$ is [18]

$$H_{\mu\nu\lambda} = \partial_\mu B_{\nu\lambda} + \partial_\nu B_{\lambda\mu} + \partial_\lambda B_{\mu\nu} \qquad (2.29)$$

The action of the complex scalar field is given by

$$S[\phi, \partial^\mu \phi] = S_0 + S_1 \qquad (2.30)$$

with

$$S_0[F, \partial^\mu F, \partial^\mu \chi] = \int d^4x \left[\partial^\mu F \partial_\mu F + F^2 \partial^\mu \chi \partial_\mu \chi - V(F^2) \right]$$

(2.31)

$$S_1[F^2, b^\mu] = \int d^4x F^2 b^\mu b_\mu$$

where S_0 describes the potential flow of the superfluid, and S_1 specifically describes the quantized vorticity. To pass from field theory to string theory, we transform S_1, through a canonical transformation, from the gauge field b^μ to the string variable $B^{\lambda\rho}$ [20]:

$$S_1 \to \tilde{S}_1$$

(2.32)

$$\tilde{S}_1 = -\frac{1}{12} \int d^4x F^2 H_{\mu\nu\lambda} H^{\mu\nu\lambda} + \pi \int F^2 B_{\mu\nu} d\sigma^{\mu\nu}$$

The first term results from a substitution of (2.28) into S_1, and the second term comes from a term $-dG/dt$, where G is the generator of the canonical transformation, needed to preserve the canonical form of the equations of motion.

The complete action undergoes the transformation $S \to \hat{S}$, where

$$\tilde{S} = S_0 - \frac{1}{12} \int d^4x F^2 H_{\mu\nu\lambda} H^{\mu\nu\lambda} + \pi \int F^2 B_{\mu\nu} d\sigma^{\mu\nu} \qquad (2.33)$$

The first term S_0 describes potential superfluid flow. The last two terms (without the factor F^2 in the integrand) constitute the Kalb–Ramond action [18], derived originally in a different context. The mathematical objects described by $B_{\mu\nu}$ are called "cosmic strings" in the literature. When the F^2 factor is present, the cosmic string is said to be "coupled to a scalar field". In our theory, of course, they all arise from the same order parameter, and are inseparable.

We emphasize again that the above is no more than a rewriting of the NLKG, and for numerical studies, it is more efficient to solve the NLKG directly.

References

[1] K. S. Schwarz, *Phys. Rev. B* **31**, 5782 (1985); *Phys. Rev.* **38**, 2389 (1988).

[2]   R. P. Feynman, in *Progress in Low Temperature Physics, Vol.1*, ed. C. J. Gorter (North-Holland, Amsterdam, 1955), p.17.

[3]   D. Lathrop, *Phys. Today*, 3 June, 2010.

[4]   G. D. Holman, *Phys. Today*, **65**, 56 (2012).

[5]   J. Koplik and H. Levine, *Phys. Rev. Lett.* **71**, 1375 (1993).

[6]   D. Kivotides, C. F. Barenghi, D. C. Samuels, *Phys. Rev. Lett.* **87**, 155301 (2001).

[7]   J. Maurer and P. Tabeling, *Europhys. Lett.* **43**, 29 (1998).

[8]   S. R. Stalp, L. Skrbek, R. J. Donnelly, *Phys. Rev. Lett.* **82**, 4831 (1999).

[9]   M. Kobayashi and M. Tsubota, *Phys. Rev. Lett.* **38**, 2398 (1988).

[10] K. Huang, *Lectures on Statistical Physics and Protein Folding* (World Scentific Publishing, Singapore, 2005), Chap. 14.

[11] M. S. Paoletti, M. E. Fisher, K. R. Sreenivasan, D. P. Lathrop, *Phys. Rev. Lett.* **101**, 154501 (2008).

[12] N. G. Berlof and B. V. Svistunov, *Phys. Rev.* **66**, 013603 (2002).

[13] W. F. Vinen, *Proc. Roy. Soc. London A* **114** (1957); **240**, 128 (1957); **243**, 400 (1957).

[14] S. K. Nemirovskii and W. Fizdon, *Rev. Mod. Phys.* **67**, 37 (1995).

[15] A. Vilenkin and E. P. S. Shellard, *Cosmic Strings and Other Topological Defects* (Cambridge University Press, 1994).

[16] B. Gradwohl, G. Kalbermann, T. Piran, E. Bertschinger, *Nucl. Phys. B* **338**, 371 (1990).

[17] C. Xiong and K. Huang, Relativistic two-fluid hefrodyamics with quantized vorticity from the nonlinear Klein–Gordon equation. (To be published.)

[18] M. Kalb and P. Ramond, *Phys. Rev. D* **9**, 2273 (1974).

[19] C. Pathinayake, A. Villenkin, B. Allen, *Phys. Rev. D* **37**, 2872, (1988).

[20] R. L. Davis and E. P. S. Shellard, *Phys. Lett. B* **214**, 219 (1988).

3 Higgs

3.1 Why Higgs

In the standard model of particle theory, the vacuum is filled with a complex scalar field called the Higgs field, introduced to give mass to the vector bosons that mediate the weak interactions, like the order parameter in superconductivity that gives mass to the photon, as discussed in Chapter 1. We review again how this Higgs mechanism works, emphasizing the importance of gauge invariance.

According to the gauge principle, a charge particle must have a Lagrangian density that is invariant under a global gauge transformation before it can be coupled to the electromagnetic field. The global gauge transformation belongs to the group $U(1)$:

$$q \to e^{i\theta} q$$

where q is the field of the charged particle, and θ is an arbitrary real constant. The electromagnetic interaction is turned on through the replacement

$$\partial^\mu q \to (\partial^\mu - ieA^\mu) q \tag{3.1}$$

where A^μ is the vector potential, or photon field. The invariance under $U(1)$ global gauge transformations is now promoted to an invariance under $U(1)$ local gauge transformations:

$$q \rightarrow e^{iex}q$$
$$A^\mu \rightarrow A^\mu - i\partial^\mu \chi \qquad (3.2)$$

where $\chi(x)$ is an arbitrary function of spacetime, and e the charge. For this reason A^μ is called a gauge field.

To make A^μ a dynamical field with its own equation of motion, we need to add to the Lagrangian density a "free-field" term $-\frac{1}{4}F^{\mu\nu}F_{\mu\nu}$, where $F^{\mu\nu} = \partial^\mu A^\nu - \partial^\nu A^\mu$ is the electromagnetic field strength. It is of course locally gauge invariant, and leads to the free-field equation of motion

$$\partial^\nu\partial_\nu A^\mu = 0 \qquad (3.3)$$

This implies that the photon is massless. A mass term would make the equation read

$$\left(\partial^\nu\partial_\nu - m^2\right)A^\mu = 0 \qquad (3.4)$$

and violate gauge invariance.

As we can see from the GL equation (1.21), a superconductor coupled to the electromagnetic field is a locally gauge invariant system. Nevertheless, the photon develops mass inside the superconductor, as implied by the Meissner effect, which shows that a magnetic field can penetrate the superconductor only to skin depth equal to the photon's inverse mass. How can we reconcile this seeming paradox? The answer is to break the local gauge symmetry *spontaneously*, by introducing a complex order parameter ψ. This leads to (3.4), in which m^2 is not a fixed constant, but proportional to $\psi^*\psi$.

In the standard model of particle physics [1], all interactions arise through a generalization of the gauge principle. In the electroweak sector, the gauge fields involved include A^μ, W^μ, and Z^μ, and the gauge group is $U(1) \times SU(2)$. Local gauge invariance requires the vector bosons W and Z to be massless, but they have been observed to have mass, with $m_W \approx 80$ GeV, $m_Z \approx 91$ GeV. This calls for a spontaneous breaking of the local $U(1) \times SU(2)$ by introducing the Higgs field $\hat{\Phi}(\mathbf{x})$, a multi-component scalar quantum field with non-vanishing vacuum expectation value

$$\phi_0 = \langle 0| \hat{\Phi}(x) |0\rangle \qquad (3.5)$$

which serves as an order parameter. The excitation of this field, the Higgs boson, has been observed, with mass $m_H \approx 125$ GeV.

By spacetime translational invariance, ϕ_0 must be uniform and time-independent; but when the system is perturbed by an external source, it can become a function of spacetime

$$\phi(x) = \langle t| \hat{\Phi}(x) |t\rangle \qquad (3.6)$$

where $|t\rangle$ is the state that evolves in time t under external perturbation. Then, masses generated from the Higgs mechanism will depend on spacetime. We often refer to $\phi(x)$ as the Higgs field.

3.2 The vorticon

We have seen in Chapter 1 that a projectile shot into superfluid helium can create a vortex ring and be trapped by it, forming a new structure (see Fig. 1.8). In a similar manner, an energetic Z can tear through the vacuum Higgs field, create a vortex ring in the Higgs field, and be trapped by it, as illustrated in Fig. 3.1. The Z is massive outside of the vortex ring, but massless inside, like a photon confined to a donut-shaped waveguide. This particle is dubbed the "vorticon", whose mass can be estimated by constructing normal modes of the Z field inside the waveguide, and minimizing the energy of the lowest mode by varying the dimensions of the waveguide [2].

The standard-model Hamiltonian in the Z sector is given by

$$H = \int d^3x \left[\frac{1}{2} \left(\mathbf{B}^2 + \mathbf{E}^2 \right) + \left| \left(\nabla - iq\mathbf{Z} \right) \phi \right|^2 + V\left(\phi^*\phi \right) \right] \qquad (3.7)$$

A Superfluid Universe

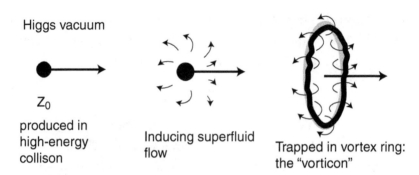

Higgs vacuum

Z_0

produced in high-energy collison

Inducing superfluid flow

Trapped in vortex ring: the "vorticon"

Fig. 3.1   A Z vector boson created in a high-energy collision induces superfluid flow in the background Higgs field, creating a vortex ring, and is trapped by it, resulting in an unstable particle, the "vorticon", with a mass of approximately 3 TeV, and a lifetime of the order of 3×10^{-25}s.

Here, ϕ is the Higgs field, $\mathbf{Z}$ the vector potential in Coulomb gauge $(\nabla \cdot \mathbf{Z} = 0)$, and $\mathbf{B} = \nabla \times \mathbf{Z}$, $\mathbf{E} = -\partial \mathbf{Z}/\partial t$. The Higgs potential $V(\phi^*\phi)$ is given by a phenomenological ϕ^4 potential:

$$V\left(\phi^*\phi\right) = \frac{\lambda}{2}\left(\phi^*\phi - F_0^2\right)^2 \tag{3.8}$$

where

$$\begin{aligned} F_0 &= 174 \text{ GeV} \\ m_H &= \sqrt{2\lambda}F_0 = 125 \text{ GeV} \\ \lambda &= 0.256 \end{aligned} \tag{3.9}$$

The gauge coupling constant q and the Z mass are given by

$$q = -\frac{e}{\sin 2\theta_W} \tag{3.10}$$

$$m_Z = \frac{gF_0}{\sqrt{2}\cos\theta_W} = 91 \text{ GeV} \tag{3.11}$$

where e is electronic charge, and θ_W is the Weinberg angle given by $\sin^2\theta_W \approx 1/4$.

There are two types of vorticons: magnetic and electric, with the magnetic (electric) field pointing along the toroidal direction. As in electromagnetic wave guides, there is no completely transverse mode. The masses are found to be

$$\frac{M_{\text{mag}}}{m_Z} = 35.3 + 6.42 \left(\frac{m_H}{m_Z}\right)^{2/3} - 1.03 \left(\frac{m_H}{m_Z}\right)^{1/2}$$

$$\frac{M_{\text{elec}}}{m_Z} = 27.7 + 5.66 \left(\frac{m_H}{m_Z}\right)^{2/3} + 0.504 \left(\frac{m_H}{m_Z}\right)^{1/2} \tag{3.12}$$

With the experimental values $m_Z = 91$ GeV and $m_H = 125$ GeV, we have

$$M_{\text{mag}} = 3.47 \text{ TeV}$$

$$M_{\text{elec}} = 2.88 \text{ TeV} \tag{3.13}$$

The size of these vorticons are of order $m_Z^{-1} \approx 10^{-12}$ cm. They are unstable, with lifetimes of the order of the Z lifetime 3×10^{-25}s.

3.3 The Higgs field as order parameter

Regardless of the ultimate microscopic origin of the Higgs field, it serves as order parameter for superfluidity on the large scale, and makes the entire universe a superfluid. But the Higgs field is introduced in particle physics with a typical length scale 10^{-13} cm, whereas we are contemplating its manifestation in the universe, with a length scale in millions of light years, or the order of 10^{20}cm. Over such a vast difference in length scale, the nature of the Higgs field could change.

There may be more vacuum fields arising from deeper layers in the structure of matter, so that the universe may contain a mixture of superfluids, like a mixture of liquid ^{4}He and ^{3}He. But we shall bypass the intricacies of particle physics, and consider here a generic vacuum complex scalar field $\phi(x)$ with a Lagrangian on a microscopic scale given by a ϕ^4 theory:

$$\mathcal{L}_{\text{micro}} = \left(\partial^\mu + iqZ^\mu\right) \phi^* \left(\partial_\mu - iqZ_\mu\right) \phi - V\left(\phi^*\phi\right) \tag{3.14}$$

where Z^μ is a generic gauge field, and $V(\phi^*\phi)$ is given by (3.8). Expanding this, we get

$$\mathcal{L}_{\text{micro}} = \partial^\mu \phi^* \partial_\mu \phi - V(\phi^*\phi) + Z_\mu j^\mu + q^2 Z^\mu Z_\mu \phi^* \phi \qquad (3.15)$$

where

$$j^\mu = iq \left(\phi^* \partial_\mu \phi - \phi \partial^\mu \phi^* \right) \qquad (3.16)$$

is a conserved current density: $\partial_\mu j^\mu = 0$.

We see matter in bulk on a macroscopic scale, and not elementary particles like the Z bosons. Even the ubiquitous electrons and photons enter the picture via macroscopic currents. Thus, the microscopic Lagrangian density should be replaced by a macroscopic one. We can replace Z^μ by a matter current density J^μ, arising from bulk matter resulting from the decay of the Z particle into electrons, neutrinos and quarks. The term $Z^\mu Z_\mu$ will be neglected, because its average value in the vacuum should be zero. Thus, on a macroscopic scale, we consider a phenomenological Lagrangian density with current–current coupling to matter:

$$\mathcal{L} = \partial^\mu \phi^* \partial_\mu \phi - V(\phi^*\phi) + J_\mu j^\mu \qquad (3.17)$$

where

$$V(\phi^*\phi) = \frac{\lambda}{2} \left(\phi^*\phi - F_0^2 \right)^2 + V_0 \qquad (3.18)$$

with λ, F_0, V_0 as phenomenological parameters different from those in (3.9). The reason is under a scale change they undergo renormalization, as we shall discuss in more detail in the next chapter. The energy density V_0 corresponds to Einstein's cosmological constant discussed in Sec. 6.2.

The equation of motion of the order parameter ϕ is a nonlinear Klein–Gordon equation (NLKG):

$$\left[\nabla^2 - \frac{\partial^2}{\partial t^2} - \lambda \left(\phi^*\phi - F_0^2 \right) \right] \phi + J^\mu \partial_\mu \phi = 0 \qquad (3.19)$$

The energy-momentum tensor is given by

$$T^{\mu\nu} = \partial^\mu \phi^* \partial^\nu \phi + \partial^\nu \phi^* \partial^\mu \phi - g^{\mu\nu} \mathcal{L} \qquad (3.20)$$

which satisfies $\partial_\mu T^{\mu\nu} = 0$.

3.4 Relativistic superfluidity

In a phase representation, we write

$$\phi(x) = F(x) e^{i\sigma(x)} \tag{3.21}$$

The superfluid 4-velocity is proportional to

$$v^\mu = \partial^\mu \sigma \tag{3.22}$$

The superfluid velocity is the 3-vector [3, 4]

$$\mathbf{v}_s = \left(\partial^0 \sigma\right)^{-1} \nabla\sigma \tag{3.23}$$

This guarantees that $|\mathbf{v}_s|$ is less than the speed of light if v^μ is a time-like 4-vector: $|\nabla\sigma|^2 < (\partial^0\sigma)^2$.

In a covariant formulation, $\mathbf{v}_s$ is part of a 4-vector W^μ [3]:

$$W^\mu = \frac{\partial^\mu \sigma}{\sqrt{-\partial^\nu \sigma \partial_\nu \sigma}} = \left(\frac{1}{\sqrt{1 - \mathbf{v}_s^2}}, \frac{\mathbf{v}_s}{\sqrt{1 - \mathbf{v}_s^2}}\right) \tag{3.24}$$

In practice, it is more convenient to work with v^μ. For example, the quantization of vorticity is a statement about $\mathbf{v}$ instead of $\mathbf{v}_s$:

$$\oint_C d\mathbf{x} \cdot \mathbf{v} = \oint_C d\mathbf{x} \cdot \nabla\sigma = 2\pi n \tag{3.25}$$

3.5 Persistence of long-ranged order

The order parameter has the value $\phi(x) = F_0$ in the lowest-energy state. One might wonder whether it really fills all space uniformly, over cosmic distances. We can only examine the effects we can think of that might destroy the long-ranged order.

Taking thermal fluctuations into account, we write $\phi(x) = F_0 + u(x)$, and expand the fluctuation in normal modes:

$$u(x) = \sum_n \int d^D k \, e^{ik \cdot x} q_n(k) \tag{3.26}$$

where D is the dimension of space, and n labels the types of modes. The integral is cut off at some upper limit. The energy residing in a normal mode is

$$E_n\,(k) = \frac{1}{2}\omega_n\,(k)\,|q_n\,(k)|^2 \qquad (3.27)$$

where ω_n is a normal frequency. The energy is equal to k_BT, by the equipartition of energy. Thus the mean-square amplitude of the nth mode is,

$$\left\langle |q_n\,(k)|^2 \right\rangle = \frac{2k_BT}{\omega_n^2\,(k)} \qquad (3.28)$$

and the mean-squared fluctuation is

$$\langle u^2 \rangle = 2k_BT \sum_n \int \frac{d^Dk}{\omega_n^2\,(k)} \qquad (3.29)$$

The dominant contribution comes from the smallest $\omega_n(k)$, which corresponds to the Goldstone mode, with $\omega_n(k) = ck$. Thus

$$\langle u^2 \rangle \sim \int dk \frac{k^{D-1}}{k^2} = \int dk\,k^{D-3} \qquad (3.30)$$

which diverges at the lower limit for $D \leq 2$, but is otherwise convergent. In other words, fluctuations in the long-wavelength Goldstone mode will destroy long-ranged order for $D \leq 2$, but not otherwise.

The other effect that could destroy long-ranged order is gravitational clumping. This is investigated in [3], which finds that gravitational effects split the Goldstone mode into two branches, analogs of the "optical" branch and "acoustical" branch in solid-state physics, as shown in Fig. 3.2. In the acoustical branch, the sound velocity becomes pure imaginary below wave number k_0, signaling that the order parameter will clump into patches of dimension $L_0 = 2\pi/k_0$; but under present conditions L_0 is much larger than the radius of the universe.

In conclusion, we expect that the phase correlation expressed by $\phi(x)$ will persist to cosmic distances in three-dimensional space.

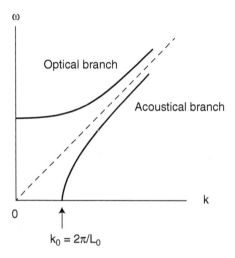

Fig. 3.2   The Goldstone modes with $\omega = ck$ are split into "optical" and "acoustical" branches by gravity. The order parameter will clump into patches of size L_0; but under present conditions in the universe, L_0 is much larger than the radius of the universe.

3.6   Non-relativistic limit

In the non-relativistic limit, ϕ has a large frequency ω corresponding to $\sigma = \omega t$. This gives a mass scale $mc^2 = \hbar\omega$. The relativistic field contains both signs of the frequency: $\phi = e^{-i\omega t}\Psi^+ + e^{i\omega t}\Psi^-$, and the second term can be neglected when ω is large. Thus

$$\phi \approx \exp\left(-\frac{imc^2 t}{\hbar}\right)\Psi^+ = \exp\left(-\frac{imc^2 t}{\hbar}\right)\exp\left(iS(\vec{x},t)\right)|\Psi^+|$$

$$(3.31)$$

One can check that NLKG reduces to NLSE in the limit $c \to \infty$.

The superfluid velocity is defined in (3.23):

$$\mathbf{v}_s = -c^2 \frac{\nabla\sigma}{\dot{\sigma}}$$

$$(3.32)$$

where the original phase σ is now given by

$$\sigma = S(\vec{x},t) - \frac{mc^2 t}{\hbar}$$

$$(3.33)$$

Thus,

$$\nabla \sigma = \nabla S$$

$$\dot{\sigma} = \dot{S} - \frac{mc^2}{\hbar}$$ (3.34)

and

$$\mathbf{v}_s = \frac{1}{\frac{m}{\hbar} - \frac{\dot{S}}{c^2}} \nabla S \xrightarrow[c \to \infty]{} \frac{\hbar}{m} \nabla S$$ (3.35)

References

[1] K. Huang, *Quarks, Leptons, and Gauge Fields*, 2nd ed. (World Scientific, Singapore, 1992).
[2] K. Huang and R. Tipton, *Phys. Rev.* **23**, 3050 (1981).
[3] K. Huang, C. Xiong, X. Zhao, *J. Mod. Phys. A* **29**, 1450074 (2014); arXiv: 1304.1595.
[4] C. Xiong, M. Good, X.Liu, K. Huang, *Phys. Rev. D* **90**, 125019 (2014); arXiv:1408.0779.

4 Renormalization

4.1 Virtual processes in quantum field theory

In quantum field theory, there are quantum fluctuations, due to virtual processes that do not exist in classical field theory. These virtual processes occur in the vacuum all the time. An electron would feel it and exhibit observable effects such as the Lamb shift and the anomalous magnetic moment. The virtual processes have a momentum spectrum that extend to infinity, and we must cut off the high end at some momentum Λ_0, or else they cause divergences in scattering matrix elements. In any event, the high-momentum end of the theory does not accurately represent the physics that it is meant to model.

The cutoff Λ_0 marks the momentum scale at which the field theory is expected to fail to represent the physics, and is usually much higher than the scale we are working with. We therefore try to lower it to an effective cutoff Λ to suit our applications. This procedure is known as renormalization, in which the coupling constants in the Lagrangian change to compensate for the change in cutoff, so as to preserve the identity of the theory [1].

45

The order parameter we consider in the last chapter is the vacuum expectation value of a quantum scalar field, and is therefore subject to renormalization.

4.2 Wilson's theory of renormalization

A complete description of the quantum field theory is given by the partition function, which is a functional integral [2]:

$$Z[J] = \mathcal{N} \int D\phi \exp\left(\frac{i}{\hbar}S[\phi] + (\phi, J)\right) \tag{4.1}$$

For illustration, we take $\phi(x)$ to be a real field, with classical action

$$S[\phi] = \int d^4x \mathcal{L}(\phi, \partial^\mu \phi) \tag{4.2}$$

where $\mathcal{L}$ is the Lagrangian density, and $\mathcal{N}$ is a normalization constant. The field is coupled to an external source $J(x)$, with $(\phi, J) = \int dx\, \phi J$. We can obtain all the correlation functions of the theory by taking repeated functional derivatives of $\ln Z$ with respect to $J(x)$:

$$\langle \phi(x_1) \cdots \phi(x_n) \rangle_0 = \frac{1}{n!} \frac{\delta}{\delta J(x_1) \cdots \delta J(x_n)} \ln Z[J]\,|_{J=0} \tag{4.3}$$

where $\langle\rangle_0$ denotes functional average with weight $S[\phi]$. This is equal to the "vacuum Green's function", the time-ordered product of the corresponding quantum operators in the vacuum state. These correlation functions determine the quantum field theory. We shall take $J \equiv 0$, since it is not relevant to our purpose, and work with $Z = Z[0]$.

We place the system in a large box, with periodic boundary conditions, and decompose $\phi(x)$ into discrete Fourier components ϕ_k. The function integral is then the integration over all ϕ_k:

$$\int D\phi = \prod_{|k|<\Lambda_0} \int_{-\infty}^{\infty} d\phi_k \tag{4.4}$$

where Λ_0 is the cutoff.

In Wilson's method [2], we lower the cutoff Λ_0 to Λ by integrating over modes with momenta lying between Λ_0 and Λ.

$$Z = \mathcal{N} \int \prod_{|k|<\Lambda_0} d\phi_k \exp\left(\frac{i}{\hbar} S[\phi]\right)$$

$$= \mathcal{N} \int \prod_{|k|<\Lambda} d\phi_k \int \prod_{\Lambda<|k|<\Lambda_0} d\phi_k \exp\left(\frac{i}{\hbar} S[\phi]\right)$$

$$\equiv \mathcal{N}' \int \prod_{|k|<\Lambda} d\phi_k \exp\left(\frac{i}{\hbar} S'[\phi]\right) \tag{4.5}$$

This is a coarse-graining process that defines a new action S', corresponding to a renormalized system with a lower cutoff Λ. The coupling parameters in S' are generally different from those in S. Thus, the appearance system is changed, even if the basic identity of the system remains the same. This process is illustrated in Fig. 4.1.

It might appear that coarse-graining goes only in one direction; but once we have defined S' for any $\Lambda < \Lambda_0$, we can change Λ in any direction. We can thus regard the scaling operations as a group, the renomalization group (RG).

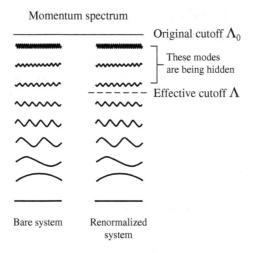

Fig. 4.1   In Wilson's theory, renormalization consists of "hiding" high-momentum modes, by integrating over them in the partition function, thereby lowering the effective cutoff.

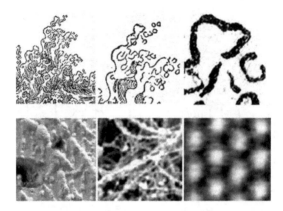

Fig. 4.2 When we examine a woodcut under increasing magnification, we are viewing it at an ever decreasing length scale. At each stage, the system presents to us a different physical appearance. First we see art, then paper fibers, and then atoms. This is like a system on a RG trajectory being described by different effective Lagrangians at different points of the trajectory.

4.3 RG trajectories

When Λ changes, the renormalized parameters in S' trace out an RG trajectory in the parameter space, the space of all possible Lagrangians. The same system may present very different physical appearances at different points on an RG trajectory. For example, Fig. 4.2 shows a woodcut under ever greater magnification, corresponding to ever decreasing length scale. At first one sees art, perhaps, then paper fibers, and then atoms.

4.4 Fixed points

The cutoff Λ does not explicitly appear in the Lagrangian, because it is a scale parameter, and may be "scaled away" by choosing the right units. Its value is solely reflected through the coupling parameters. One cannot "send it to infinity" by declaration; it approaches infinity only when the parameters are so tuned that the correlation

UV fixed point
$\Lambda = \infty$

Fig. 4.3   UV trajectory. The arrow points along the coarse-graining direction, and the ticks make equal decrements in the effective cutoff Λ. The original cutoff Λ_0 can be made infinite by placing it at the fixed point. For a theory on UV trajectory, one can fulfill the dream of "sending the cutoff to infinity."

length of the system approaches infinity. This occurs at a fixed point of the RG group, corresponding to a scale-invariant system.

By convention, we take the positive direction on an RG trajectory to that of coarse-graining, or the direction along which Λ decreases. Fixed points are terminals of trajectories, and RG trajectories never cross themselves, nor each other, except at these fixed points. Interactions usually vanish at a fixed point, because it corresponds to a scale-invariant system, and we will make that assumption.

4.5   Asymptotic freedom

A trajectory that comes out of a fixed point upon coarse-graining is called a UV (ultraviolet) trajectory, as illustrated in Fig. 4.3. A system located on an UV trajectory is "asymptotically free", for the interaction vanishes as $\Lambda \rightarrow \infty$. This is the case for QCD. In this case, one can make the original cutoff Λ_0 infinite by placing it at the UV fixed point.

4.6   Triviality

A trajectory that goes into a fixed point upon coarse-graining is called an IR (infrared) trajectory. On the entire IR trajectory we have $\Lambda = \infty$, because Λ can only decrease along the coarse-graining direction, and $\Lambda = \infty$ at the fixed point. It is not a trajectory at all, but

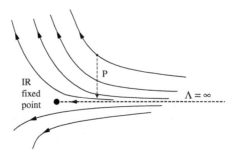

Fig. 4.4 The dotted line represents an IR trajectory, which is a limiting trajectory that is a boundary between two phases of the system. Any point on this trajectory is equivalent to the fixed point, with $\Lambda = \infty$. One can approach the fixed point by going along a path P, on which the system falls like a rock into a bottomless canyon.

a limiting one that is a boundary separating two different phases, for example one with spontaneous symmetry and one without. One cannot place a system on it, but only approach it along some path P, as shown in Fig. 4.4. The RG trajectories on both sides of the dotted line are like rock strata on the sides of an infinitely deep canyon. The path P drops into the canyon towards the unreachable bottom, where $\Lambda = \infty$.

If the interaction vanishes at an IR fixed point, as we assume, then it vanishes along the entire IR trajectory, where the system becomes a free theory. This is the case for QED and the ϕ^4 interaction, a situation known as "triviality".[1]

But triviality happens only if one insists that the original cutoff Λ_0 be infinite. In practice, whether or not Λ_0 is infinite hardly matters. In QED, for example, one takes the electron's physical charge from experiments. This means that Λ_0 has some finite value

---

[1]Landau [3] says that, by virtue of "triviality", quantum field theory predicts that the electron's charge is zero. Hamiltonian field theory is therefore dead, and "should be buried with honors." This was when quantum field theory fell out of fashion, under siege from bootstrap theory and "nuclear democracy". It took Wilson's insight into the physical meaning of renormalization, and the experimental evidence for quarks to restore faith in quantum field theory, in the form of the standard model.

determined by the electron's charge, but it is irrelevant. Conceptually, this make the theory "phenomenological" instead of "fundamental", but its predictions have agreed with experiments to the precision of one part in a trillion.

In the end, all theories are phenomenological to different degrees. Whether the actual fundamental theory exists is a question belonging to the realm of metaphysics.

4.7 Polchinski's equation

Wilson's renormalization theory relies on a sharp high-momentum cutoff. Polchinski [4] gives a reformulation that is independent of the form of the cutoff, and obtains a functional integro-differential equation for the interaction Lagrangian.

The virtual modes in quantum field theory are described by the propagator function, which for a free field has Fourier transform $\Delta(k^2) = k^{-2}$. We can introduce a cutoff by modifying the high k behavior, replacing it with

$$\Delta(k^2) = \frac{f(k^2/\Lambda^2)}{k^2}$$

$$f(z) \underset{z\to\infty}{\to} 0 \tag{4.6}$$

The cutoff Λ appears as a scale parameter in the function $f(k^2/\Lambda^2)$, whose inverse Fourier transform will be denoted by $K(x, \Lambda)$. Its detailed form is not important for our development.

Consider a real scalar field $\phi(x)$ in d-dimensional Euclidean spacetime, with Lagrangian density

$$\mathcal{L} = \mathcal{L}_0 + \mathcal{L}' \tag{4.7}$$

where $\mathcal{L}_0$ is the free-field Lagrangian density, and $\mathcal{L}'$ the interaction Lagrangian density. The classical action is

$$S[\phi, \Lambda] = S_0[\phi, \Lambda] + S'[\phi, \Lambda] \tag{4.8}$$

where the first term corresponds to the free field, and the term $S'[\phi, \Lambda]$ represents interactions. The free field term can be put in the form

$$S_0[\phi, \Lambda] = \frac{1}{2} \int d^d x d^d y\, \phi(x) K^{-1}(x - y, \Lambda) \phi(y) \qquad (4.9)$$

where $K^{-1}(x - y, \Lambda)$ is the inverse of the propagator function $K(x - y, \Lambda)$ in an operator sense:

$$\int d^d z\, K(x - z) K^{-1}(z - y) = (2\pi)^d \delta^d(x - y) \qquad (4.10)$$

The operator K^{-1} differs from the Laplacian operator significantly only in a neighborhood of $|x - y| = 0$, of radius Λ^{-1}.

The partition function with external source J is given by

$$Z[J, \Lambda] = \mathcal{N} \int D\phi\, e^{-S[\phi, \Lambda] - (J, \phi)} \qquad (4.11)$$

where $(J, \phi) = \int d^d x J(x) \phi(x)$, and $\mathcal{N}$ is a normalization constant that may depend on Λ. Renormalization means that, when Λ changes, the interaction term S' changes in such a manner as to preserve the theory. That is, $Z[J, \Lambda]$ actually is independent of Λ:

$$\frac{dZ[J, \Lambda]}{d\Lambda} = 0 \qquad (4.12)$$

This is solved by Polchinski's renormalization equation, which for $J \equiv 0$ reads as

$$\frac{dS'}{d\Lambda} = -\frac{1}{2} \int dx dy \frac{\partial K(x - y, \Lambda)}{\partial \Lambda} \left[\frac{\delta^2 S'}{\delta \phi(x) \delta \phi(y)} - \frac{\delta S'}{\delta \phi(x)} \frac{\delta S'}{\delta \phi(y)} \right]$$

$$(4.13)$$

One can determine $S'[\phi, \Lambda]$ by solving this functional integro-differential equation, with given initial condition at $\Lambda = \Lambda_0$. It is this initial condition that distinguishes different systems. One can extract the interaction Lagrangian density $\mathcal{L}'$, which generates the RG trajectories.

References

[1] K. Huang, *Int. J. Mod. Phys. A* **30**, 1530056 (2015); arXiv:1508.05619 [hep-th].

[2] K. Huang, *Quantum Field Theory, from Operators to Path Integrals*, 2nd ed. (Wiley-VCH,Weinheim, Germany, 2010).

[3] L. D. Landau, in *Niels Bohr and the Development of Physics*, ed. W. Pauli (McGraw-Hill, New York, 1955).

[4] J. Polchinski, *Nucl. Phys. B* **231**, 269 (1984).

5 Halpern–Huang scalar field

5.1 The Gaussian fixed point

A free massless scalar field is scale-invariant, corresponding to a fixed point of RG called the Gaussian fixed point. RG trajectories issue forth from this fixed point, in all directions in the space of all possible Lagrangians. There are trajectories emanating along non-trivial directions, and these are UV trajectories on which the scalar field is asymptotically free. IR trajectories correspond to trivial directions, on which the system remains a massless free field. There are, of course, trajectories that go by the Gaussian fixed point without ever touching it, an example of which is the ϕ^4 theory. With decreasing or increasing length scale along its trajectory, the system sails off to infinity to realms unknown. These possibilities are illustrated in Fig. 5.1.

The scalar field that permeates the universe was described in Chapter 3 by ϕ^4 theory. That is merely a convenient phenomenological choice for a specific scale. If the scalar field emerges at the big bang from the Gaussian fixed point, then it must do so along a nontrivial direction.

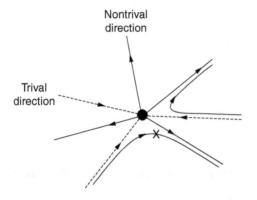

Fig. 5.1   The black dot denotes the Gaussian fixed point in the space of all possible Lagrangians, corresponding to a massless free scalar field. The trivial directions correspond to IR trajectories, on which the scalar field remains free and massless. The nontrivial directions correspond to UV trajectories, on which the scalar field is asymptotically free. A ϕ^4 theory corresponds to the cross on a trajectory that never touches the Gaussian fixed point.

5.2   Eigenpotential

To search for nontrivial directions from the Gaussian fixed point, we examine the eigenvalues of RG transformations at the fixed point. Consider for simplicity a real scalar field $\phi(x)$, with Lagrangian density

$$\mathcal{L} = \partial^\mu \phi \partial_\nu \phi - V \tag{5.1}$$

The free action S_0 and interaction action S' are given by

$$S_0 = \int d^d x \partial^\mu \phi \partial_\nu \phi$$
$$S' = \int d^d x V \tag{5.2}$$

The high-momentum cutoff Λ is the only scale in the theory. We can define a dimensionless field φ and dimensionless potential U in d-dimensional spacetime:

$$\varphi(x) = \Lambda^{1-d/2}\phi(x)$$
$$U = \Lambda^{-d}V \tag{5.3}$$

At the Gaussian fixed point $S' \equiv 0$, and in its neighborhood we can linearize the Polchinski equation, obtaining

$$\frac{dS'}{d\Lambda} \approx -\frac{1}{2} \int dxdy \frac{\partial K(x-y,\Lambda)}{\partial\Lambda} \frac{\delta^2 S'}{\delta\phi(x)\delta\phi(y)} \qquad (5.4)$$

Assume that S' can be put in the form

$$S'[\phi,\Lambda] = -\Lambda^d \int d^dx U(\varphi(x),\Lambda) \qquad (5.5)$$

Substituting this into the linearized Polchinski equation yields a linear differential equation for $U(\varphi,\Lambda)$:

$$\Lambda\frac{\partial U}{\partial\Lambda} + \frac{\kappa}{2}U'' + \left(1-\frac{d}{2}\right)\varphi U' + Ud = 0 \qquad (5.6)$$

where $U' = \partial U/\partial\varphi$, and $\kappa = \Lambda^{3-d}\partial K(0,\Lambda)/\partial\Lambda$.

At the Gaussian fixed point $U \equiv 0$. Along directions corresponding to principal axes, we have eigenpotentials with the behavior

$$\Lambda\frac{\partial U_b}{\partial\Lambda} = -bU_b \qquad (5.7)$$

where b is the eigenvalue, with $b > 0$ corresponding to asymptotic freedom. This equation is a linear approximation to the more general relation

$$\Lambda\frac{\partial U_b}{\partial\Lambda} = \beta[U_b] \qquad (5.8)$$

where β is a functional.

Substituting (5.7) into (5.6), we obtain the differential equation

$$\left[\frac{\kappa}{2}\frac{d^2}{d\varphi^2} - \frac{1}{2}(d-2)\varphi\frac{d}{d\varphi} + (d-b)\right]U_b = 0 \qquad (5.9)$$

The cutoff Λ enters only through the normalization of U_b and the parameter κ, which can be scaled away. In view of (5.7), the normalization factor is Λ^{-b}.

For $d = 2$, (5.9) gives a sinusoidal solution, and the theory reduces to the XY model, or equivalently the sine-Gordon theory.

For $d \neq 2$, (5.9) can be transformed into Kummer's equation:

$$\left[z \frac{d^2}{dz^2} + (q - z) \frac{d}{dz} - p \right] U_b(z) = 0 \qquad (5.10)$$

where

$$q = 1/2$$
$$p = \frac{b - d}{d - 2} \qquad (5.11)$$
$$z = \frac{d - 2}{2\kappa} \varphi^2$$

The solution is

$$U_b(z) = c\Lambda^{-b} \left[M(p, q, z) - 1 \right] \qquad (5.12)$$

where c is an arbitrary constant, and M is the Kummer function. We have subtracted 1 to make $U_b(0) = 0$. This is permissible, since it merely changes the normalization of the partition function.

We quote the generalization to an N-component scalar field with $O(N)$ symmetry, with components $\varphi_1, \ldots, \varphi_N$:

$$U_b(z) = c\Lambda^{-b} \left[M\left(\frac{b - d}{d - 2}, \frac{N}{2}, z \right) - 1 \right]$$
$$z = \frac{d - 2}{2\kappa} \sum_{n=1}^{N} \varphi_n^2 \qquad (5.13)$$

This is the Halpern–Huang potential. It was originally derived by summing one-loop Feynman diagrams [1] with sharp cutoff, for which $(d - 2)/2\kappa = 8\pi$. The improved derivation here, for arbitrary cutoff function using Polchinski's equation, is due to Periwal [2].

The Kummer function has the power series

$$M(p, q, z) = 1 + \frac{p}{q}z + \frac{p(p+1)}{q(q+1)} \frac{z^2}{2!} + \frac{p(p+1)(p+2)}{q(q+1)(q+2)} \frac{z^3}{3!} + \cdots \qquad (5.14)$$

This function reduces to a polynomial for negative integer p. Otherwise it has exponential asymptotic behavior for large z:

$$M(p, q, z) \approx \frac{\Gamma(q)}{\Gamma(p)} z^{p-q} e^z \qquad (5.15)$$

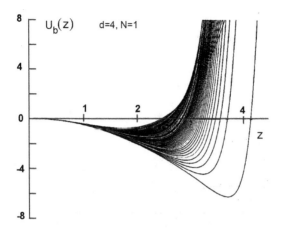

Fig. 5.2 A family of eigenpotentials in the acceptable range. They increase exponentially at large values of z. The scale on the vertical axis is arbitrary.

5.3 Asymptotic freedom

Asymptotic freedom requires $b > 0$. From (5.11) for $d = 4$, this implies $p > -2$. Thus the only possibility that asymptotically free theory has a polynomial potential corresponds to $p = -1$, or $b = 2$. But this is a free-field theory with mass. Therefore, no scalar field theory with polynomial potentials, except for the free field, can be asymptotically free.[1]

We also require spontaneous symmetry breaking, i.e. that U_b have a minimum at finite φ. Therefore the acceptable range of b is

$$0 < b < 2 \tag{5.16}$$

Figure 5.2 shows plots of eigenpotentials in the acceptable range. In Fig. 5.3, an eigenpotential is compared to polynomials obtained by truncating the power series.

---

[1] The ϕ^4 theory corresponds to $b = 0$, which seems to indicate that it borders on asymptotic freedom; but this is true only in the linear approximation. Higher correction gives $\Lambda \frac{\partial U_0}{\partial \Lambda} = \frac{3}{16\pi^2} U_0^2$ which indicates it is not asymptotically free [3].

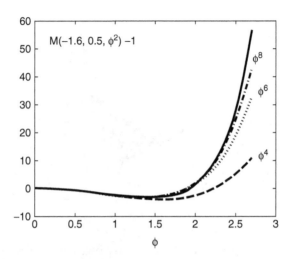

Fig. 5.3 Solid curve is the eigenpotential with eigenvalue $b = 0.8$. The other curves are polynomials obtained by truncating the power series at ϕ^4, ϕ^6, ϕ^8.

5.4 Superposition of eigenpotentials

The field potential U may be a linear superposition of eigenpotentials, since the defining equation (5.7) is linear. Consider $d = 4$, $N = 1$, and

$$U(z) = c_1 U_{0.4}(z) - c_2 U_1(z) \tag{5.17}$$

The eigenpotential is always negative near $z = 0$, and the slope is more negative for larger b. In the above, the second term is positive at small z because of the minus sign, and dominates over the first term. The first term eventually catches up, and controls the asymptotic exponential behavior. The qualitative behavior is illustrated in Fig. 5.4. The potential is positive at small z, turns negative and goes through a minimum, and eventually rises exponentially. Because U_b is proportional to Λ^b, the weight shifts to the second term for large Λ. This delays the occurrence of the minimum as z increases, but it happens very suddenly, and the minimum becomes extremely narrow and deep. Figure 5.4 shows z_{min} and $U(z_{min})$ as functions

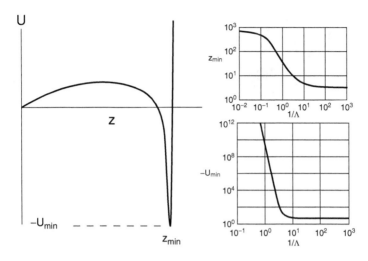

Fig. 5.4   Superposition of two eigenpotentials to produce a potential U with very deep and narrow minima at $\pm z_{mn}$, with minimum value U_{min}. The field flip-flops between $\pm z_{mn}$, like an Ising spin.

of $a = \Lambda^{-1}$, for $c_2/c_1 = 50$. The field φ, being proportional to $\pm\sqrt{z}$, will be trapped between two symmetrically placed minima, and the field theory approaches the Ising spin model.

References

[1] K. Halpern and K. Huang, *Phys. Rev.* **53**, 3252 (1996).

[2] V. Periwal, J. *Mod. Phys. Lett. A* **11**, 2915 (1996); arXiv:9512108 [hep-th].

[3] K. Huang, *Quarks, Leptons, and Gauge Fields*, 2nd ed. (World Scientific, Singapore, 1992), p. 191, Eq. (9.67).

6 The dynamics of spacetime

6.1 Spacetime curvature

In Galileo's legendary experiment, he dropped two balls from atop the leaning tower of Pisa, one heavy and one light. Both hit the ground at the same time, thereby demonstrating the equivalence principle, namely that gravitational mass is equal to inertia mass. Three hundred years later, Einstein pointed out that inertial mass and gravitational mass are different concepts, and for them to be really equal, the defining concepts must be one and the same. He succeeded unifying the concepts through the theory of general relativity, in which matter moves along geodesics in curved spacetime, so that the trajectories are purely geometrical.

The basic variable describing spacetime is the metric tensor $g^{\mu\nu}(x)$, also referred to as the gravitational field, which gives the spacetime separation ds between two events at x^μ and $x^\mu + dx^\mu$:

$$ds^2 = g^{\mu\nu} dx_\mu dx_\nu \tag{6.1}$$

Under a general coordinate transformation, x_μ transforms as a vector, by definition, and the product $x_\mu x_\nu$ transforms as a tensor. A scalar field $\phi(x)$ is invariant under coordinate transformations, and its gradient $A_\mu = \partial_\mu \phi$ transforms as a vector.

63

The crucial point is that $\partial_\mu A_\nu$ is not a tensor in general. To get a tensor, one must replace the derivative ∂_μ with the covariant derivative D_μ defined by

$$D_\mu A_\nu = \partial_\mu A_\nu - \Gamma^\alpha_{\mu\nu} A_\alpha \qquad (6.2)$$

which introduces the connection $\Gamma^\alpha_{\mu\nu}$. Because of this term, D_μ and D_ν do not commute, and the commutator defines the Riemann curvature tensor $R^\lambda_{\alpha\mu\nu}$:

$$(D_\mu D_\nu - D_\nu D_\mu) A_\alpha = -R^\lambda_{\alpha\mu\nu} A_\lambda \qquad (6.3)$$

From the Riemann curvature tensor, one obtains the Ricci tensor $R^{\mu\nu}$ (or just curvature tensor), and its trace R:

$$\begin{aligned} R_{\mu\nu} &= R_{\nu\mu} = R^\alpha_{\mu\alpha\nu} \\ R &= g^{\mu\nu} R_{\mu\nu} \end{aligned} \qquad (6.4)$$

All these depend on the metric:

$$\begin{aligned} \Gamma^\alpha_{\gamma\mu} &= \frac{1}{2} g^{\alpha\beta} (\partial_\gamma g_{\beta\mu} + \partial_\mu g_{\beta\gamma} - \partial_\beta g_{\gamma\mu}) \\ R^\alpha_{\beta\gamma\delta} &= \partial_\gamma \Gamma^\alpha_{\beta\delta} - \partial_\delta \Gamma^\alpha_{\beta\gamma} + \Gamma^\alpha_{\gamma\sigma} \Gamma^\sigma_{\beta\delta} - \Gamma^\alpha_{\delta\sigma} \Gamma^\sigma_{\beta\gamma} \end{aligned} \qquad (6.5)$$

6.2   Einstein's equation

Matter is a source of spacetime curvature. Since a tensor associated with matter is the energy-momentum tensor $T^{\mu\nu}$, one might try the relation $R^{\mu\nu} \propto T^{\mu\nu}$. But this is not consistent with the conservation law $D_\mu T^{\mu\nu} = 0$. The remedy is to add a term $-\frac{1}{2} g^{\mu\nu} R$ to the curvature tensor to create the combination called the Einstein tensor

$$G^{\mu\nu} = R^{\mu\nu} - \frac{1}{2} g^{\mu\nu} R \qquad (6.6)$$

which satisfies the Bianchi identity

$$D_\mu G^{\mu\nu} \equiv 0 \qquad (6.7)$$

Now the relation $G^{\mu\nu} \propto T^{\mu\nu}$ is consistent with conservation of energy-momentum. Supplying the appropriate proportionality constant gives Einstein's equation:

$$R^{\mu\nu} - \frac{1}{2}g^{\mu\nu}R = 8\pi G T^{\mu\nu} \tag{6.8}$$

where G is Newton's constant:

$$G = 6.672 \times 10^{-11} \text{ m}^3 \text{ kg}^{-1} \text{ s}^{-2} \tag{6.9}$$

It is introduced in Einstein's equation in order that the latter recovers Newtonian gravity in the limit of a flat spacetime. The Planck scales are defined as follows:

$$\text{Planck length} = (\hbar c^{-3})^{1/2}(4\pi G)^{1/2} = 5.73 \times 10^{-35} \text{ m}$$
$$\text{Planck time} = (\hbar c^{-5})^{1/2}(4\pi G)^{1/2} = 1.91 \times 10^{-43}\text{s} \tag{6.10}$$
$$\text{Planck energy} = (\hbar c^5)^{1/2}(4\pi G)^{-1/2} = 3.44 \times 10^{18}\text{GeV}$$

In units $\hbar = c = 1$, Newton's constant is a squared length:

$$G = \frac{1}{4\pi}(\text{Planck length})^2 = 3 \times 10^{-66} \text{ cm}^2 \tag{6.11}$$

If we take $4\pi G = 1$, then length, time, and energy will all be in Planck units.

One has the freedom to add a term proportional to $g^{\mu\nu}$ in Einstein's equation, leading to

$$R^{\mu\nu} - \frac{1}{2}g^{\mu\nu}R = 8\pi G T^{\mu\nu} - \Lambda_0 g^{\mu\nu} \tag{6.12}$$

where Λ_0 is called Einstein's cosmological constant. But the $T^{\mu\nu}$ of a scalar field can give rise to such a term, for example, the vacuum energy density V_0 in the phenomenological potential (3.18) of a scalar field.

6.3 Metrics

Matter is a source of curvature, and contributes to $g^{\mu\nu}$, but it also moves along a geodesic in curved spacetime, and its equation of motion depends on $g^{\mu\nu}$. The two systems, gravitational field and matter, are coupled together, and Einstein's equation is only half the story. In cosmology, we want to trace the evolution of the universe in this coupled dynamics.

Note that even a universe devoid of matter can have nontrivial dynamics, because Einstein's equation is nonlinear, and curvature can be its own source.

To formulate a problem in general relativity, the starting point is often the adoption of an appropriate form of the metric $g^{\mu\nu}$, which captures the essence of the physical situation, yet is simple enough for analysis. So far, only a few metrics have been discovered as solutions to the Einstein's equation. They include

- The Robertson–Walker (RW) metric, which describes a spatially uniform and homogeneous universe;
- The Schwarzschild metric, which describes an empty region of spacetime outside a spherically symmetric static mass with no angular momentum;
- The Kerr metric, which is the generalization of the Schwarzschild metric to an inner mass with angular momentum;
- The DeSitter metric, which solves Einstein's equation with cosmological constant, but otherwise devoid of matter;
- The Kerr–Newman and Kerr–Nordstrom metrics, which generalize the Schwarzschild metric for an inside mass with electric charge, the former without angular momentum, and the latter with angular momentum.

6.4 The expanding universe

The RW metric describes a spatially homogeneous and isotropic universe, and is given through the line element

$$ds^2 = -dt^2 + a^2(t)\left(\frac{dr^2}{1-kr^2} + r^2 d\Omega^2\right) \qquad (k=0,\pm 1) \qquad (6.13)$$

The parameter $k = 1$ corresponds to a space with positive curvature, $k = -1$ that with negative curvature, and $k = 0$ is the limiting case of zero curvature. The spatial coordinates are spherical coordinates: $x^\mu = \{t, r, \theta, \varphi\}$, and $d\Omega^2 = d\theta^2 + \sin^2\theta d\varphi^2$ refers to an element of solid angle. Recent observations show $k = 0$ in the present universe. [See (6.25).]

The only unknown quantity in the metric is $a(t)$, the length scale of the universe. All physical lengths are proportional to $a(t)$. The coordinate r is dimensionless. It is said to be "co-moving", in that the scale $a(t)$ has been factored out. Suppose we are situated at $r = 0$, and there is a galaxy at $r = R$. The distance between us is given by

$$s = a(t) \int_0^R \frac{dr}{\sqrt{1 - kr^2}} \qquad (6.14)$$

The time dependence is contained solely in $a(t)$, which is the same for all galaxies. Thus, it will appear to us that all galaxies are moving away (or towards) us, at a rate proportional to $\dot{a}(t)$. Of course, the same must be true from the point of view of any galaxy. This prediction is consistent with the observations of Hubble [1], who finds that galaxies recede from us with velocity proportional to distance. This is known as Hubble's law:

$$H \equiv \frac{1}{a}\frac{da}{dt} \approx \frac{1}{15 \times 10^9 \text{ yrs}} \qquad (6.15)$$

where H is known as Hubble's constant. However, the sizes of galaxies will not increase with the expansion, because galactic structure involves non-gravitational forces.

The fabric of the universe is expanding, like the surface of a balloon being blown up at a constant rate, as illustrated in Fig. 6.1. As the radius $a(t)$ of the balloon increases at a constant rate, the relative velocity between p, q will be proportional to the distance between them. However, a coin glued to the balloon will not increase in size.

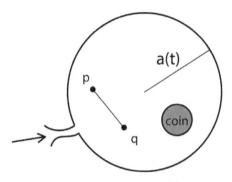

Fig. 6.1   The fabric of spacetime in an expanding universe is like the surface of a balloon being blown up. The distance between two points p and q on the surface of the balloon increases as the radius of the balloon $a(t)$ increases. The further they are separated, the faster the distance increases. An object glued to the surface, such as a coin, however, will not increase in size, because its structure has nothing to do with the fabric of the balloon.

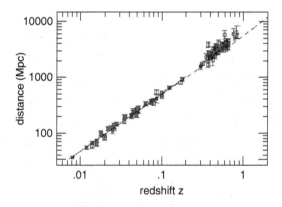

Fig. 6.2   A plot of galactic distance versus velocity (redshift) reveals that the universe is expanding. It conforms to Hubble's law corresponding to the straightline, except at the high end. Deviations indicate that the cosmic expansion accelerates with time. This suggests that the expansion is driven by some unknown "dark energy".

Observational data on the relation between galactic distance and galactic velocity (redshift) is shown in Fig. 6.2. Points at the high end deviates from the linear Hubble's law [2], and indicate that distant galaxies have slower speed than expected. Since light from these galaxies were emitted at an earlier epoch, this means that the cosmic expansion was slower then, or that the expansion is accelerating. The accelerated expansion is thought to be driven by some unknown "dark energy" [3].

6.5 Perfect-fluid cosmology

Our universe on a large scale is uniform and isotropic, and may be described by the RW metric. A simple model for matter is a classical "perfect" fluid that is uniform and isotropic. Let us describe the cosmology based on it.

The non-vanishing components of $g^{\mu\nu}$ are

$$g^{00} = -1$$

$$g^{11} = \frac{a^2}{1 - kr^2}$$

$$g^{22} = a^2 r^2 \qquad\qquad (6.16)$$

$$g^{33} = a^2 r^2 \sin^2 \theta$$

where $a(t)$ is the length scale. The determinant g is given by

$$\sqrt{-g} = \frac{a^3 r^2 \sin \theta}{\sqrt{1 - kr^2}} \qquad\qquad (6.17)$$

The curvature tensor has the following non-vanishing components

$$R_{00} = -3\frac{\ddot{a}}{a}$$

$$R_{ij} = \left[\frac{\ddot{a}}{a} + 2 \left(\frac{\dot{a}}{a} \right)^2 + \frac{k}{a^2} \right] g_{ij} \quad (i, j = 1, 2, 3)$$

$$R = 6 \left[\frac{\ddot{a}}{a} + \left(\frac{\dot{a}}{a} \right)^2 + \frac{k}{a^2} \right] \qquad\qquad (6.18)$$

$$R_{0j} = 0$$

The energy-momentum tensor of the perfect fluid is given by

$$T^{00} = -\rho$$
$$T^{ij} = g^{ij}p \quad (i,j = 1,2,3) \tag{6.19}$$
$$T^{j0} = 0$$

where ρ is the energy density, and p the pressure. With the RW metric, the conservation law $D_\mu T^{\mu\nu} = 0$ becomes

$$\dot{\rho} + \frac{3\dot{a}}{a}(\rho + p) = 0 \tag{6.20}$$

As a simple model, we assume an "equation-of-state" $p = w_0\rho$, where w_0 is a constant, having the values

$$w_0 = \begin{cases} -1 \text{ (Vacuum)} \\ 1/3 \text{ (Radiation)} \\ 0 \text{ (Pressureless dust)} \end{cases} \tag{6.21}$$

Einstein's equation has only two components:

$$\left(\frac{\dot{a}}{a}\right)^2 + \frac{k}{a^2} = -\frac{8\pi}{3}GT_{00}$$
$$\left[\frac{2\ddot{a}}{a} + \left(\frac{\dot{a}}{a}\right)^2 + \frac{k}{a^2}\right]g_{ij} = -8\pi G T_{ij} \tag{6.22}$$

In terms of Hubble's parameter H defined in (6.15), we have $\dot{a} = Ha$, and the following cosmological equations:

$$\dot{H} = \frac{k}{a^2} - 4\pi G(p + \rho)$$
$$H^2 = -\frac{k}{a^2} + \frac{8\pi G}{3}\rho \tag{6.23}$$
$$\dot{\rho} = -3H(\rho + p)$$

There are two unknowns a and p, and three equations, and the system seems to be overdetermined. Actually, the H^2 equation is a constraint of the form

$$X \equiv H^2 + \frac{k}{a^2} - \frac{8\pi G}{3}\rho = 0 \tag{6.24}$$

and the $\dot{\rho}$ equation is of the form $\dot{X} = 0$. Thus the constraint need to be applied only once, as an initial condition. These equations constitute the so-called "standard model of cosmology" [4].

The constraint (6.24) can be rewritten in the form of a sum-rule:

$$\frac{8\pi G\rho}{3H^2} - \frac{k}{H^2 a^2} = 1 \qquad (6.25)$$

Using this to analyze data from the CBM (cosmic microwave background) reveals that the first term above is within 10% of unity, hence the second term is zero, or $k = 0$, implying that our universe is flat [5].

References

[1] E. P. Hubble, *The Realm of the Nebulae* (Yale University Press, New Haven, 1936).

[2] A. G. Riess *et al.*, *Astrophys. J.* **659**, 98 (2007).

[3] P. J. E. Peebles and R. Bharat, *Rev. Mod. Phys.* **75**, 559 (2003).

[4] W. Kolb and M. S. Turner, *The Early Universe* (Addison-Wesley, Redwood City, 1990).

[5] P. de Bernardis *et al.*, *Nature* **404**, 955 (2000).

7 Black holes

7.1 The Schwarzschild radius

The most general spherically symmetric metric that satisfies Einstein's equation has the form

$$ds^2 = -f(r)\,dt^2 + \frac{1}{f(r)}dr^2 + r^2 d\Omega^2 \qquad (7.1)$$

in spherical coordinates, where $d\Omega^2 = d\theta^2 + \sin^2\theta d\varphi^2$. Note that here r is of dimension length, and not "co-moving", as in the RW metric. Substituting this form into Einstein's equation without matter, and without cosmological constant, we find

$$f(r) = 1 - \frac{2MG/c^2}{r} \qquad (7.2)$$

This defines the Schwarzschild metric. In the limit $r \to \infty$, the metric approaches a form corresponding to Newtonian gravity with a mass M at $r = 0$, without angular momentum. According to Birkoff's theorem, the spacetime outside of a spherically symmetric mass distribution is the same as that produced by a point mass at the center. This is like Gauss' theorem in electrostatics: as long you are outside, you cannot know the details inside.

A Superfluid Universe

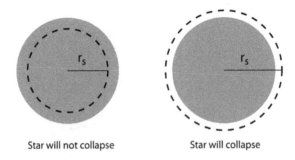

Star will not collapse   Star will collapse

Fig. 7.1   Each "star" has a Schwarzschild radius r_s proportional to its mass. (Left) The star covers r_s, and will not collapse. (Right) The star lies within r_s, and will collapse into a black hole.

The metric defines a radius r_s, at which $f(r_s) = 0$:

$$r_s = 2MG/c^2 \qquad (7.3)$$

This is called the "Schwarzschild radius". Suppose the mass distribution is confined to a sphere of radius r_0. If $r_0 > r_s$, the Schwarzschild metric ceases to be valid inside the mass distribution. On the other hand, if $r_0 < r_s$, , all matter is contained within the radius r_s, and solving Einstein's equation will show that the mass distribution undergoes gravitational collapse into what is called a "black hole". These possibilities are illustrated in Fig. 7.1.

The Schwarzschild radius of the Sun is about 3 km, and that of the Earth is about 9 nm. No danger of gravitational collapse there. But the Schwarzschild metric has been used to calculate spacetime curvature due to the Sun, and observable effects, such as the deflection of light by the Sun, and the advance of the perihelion of Mercury's orbit.

A "star" whose radius is smaller than its Schwarzschild radius will collapse. This problem was solved by Oppenheimer and Snyder [1], and reformulated by Weinberg [2]. We start with a uniform mass distribution which just fills its Schwarzschild radius, as shown in Fig. 7.2. Outside the distribution, the metric is Schwarzschild, which is a vacuum solution. Inside, we use the RW metric. The

Outside:
Schwarzschild

Inside:
Robertson-
Walker

Fig. 7.2 Oppenheimer–Snyder model of gravitational collapse. Initially, the star fits snugly into its Schwarzschild radius. The metric outside is Schwarzschild, and that inside is RW.

boundary condition is that the inside solution smoothly joins the outside solution. The aim is to find out how the boundary collapses.

7.2 Oppenheimer–Snyder solution: inside

With the RW metric, the cosmological equations inside are

$$\dot{H} = \frac{k}{a^2} - 4\pi G \left(p + \rho \right) \tag{7.4}$$

$$H^2 = \frac{8\pi G}{3} \rho - \frac{k}{a^2} \tag{7.5}$$

$$\dot{\rho} = -\frac{3\dot{a}}{a} \left(\rho + p \right) \tag{7.6}$$

where $H = \dot{a}/a$. The equations are invariant under time reversal $t \to -t$. We take as initial condition $a(0) = 1$, $\dot{a}(0) = 0$. The second equation is a constraint, and the last equation guarantees its preservation. We can solve any two of these equations, and be assured that the third one is automatically satisfied, as long as the initial conditions are consistent with the equations.

We take $p = 0$, corresponding to pressureless dust. Then (7.6) gives $\dot{\rho}/\rho = -3\dot{a}/a$, which can be integrated to yield

$$\rho = c_0 a^{-3} \tag{7.7}$$

where $c_0 > 0$ is an arbitrary constant. Substituting this into (7.5), we

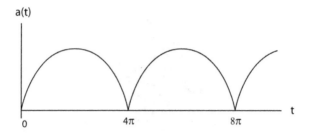

Fig. 7.3 Oppenheimer–Snyder solution. The radius of the star is a periodic function of the inside time, more specifically a cycloid. The radius goes to zero in finite time and bounces back, leading to an expanding universe. However, to an observer outside, the collapse takes infinite time.

obtain

$$\dot{a}^2 = \frac{8\pi G c_0}{3a} - k \qquad (7.8)$$

At $t = 0$, this gives

$$\frac{8\pi G c_0}{3} = k \qquad (7.9)$$

Thus, the only physically possible value of the curvature parameter is $k = 1$. Now we can write

$$\dot{a}^2 = k\left(\frac{1}{a} - 1\right) \qquad (7.10)$$

and the solution in parametric form is

$$a = \frac{1}{2}(1 + \cos\psi)$$
$$t = \frac{\psi + \sin\psi}{2\sqrt{k}} \qquad (7.11)$$

This describes a cycloid, whose graph is shown in Fig. 7.3. The radius $a(t)$ vanishes when $t = T$, where

$$T = \frac{\pi}{2\sqrt{k}} \qquad (7.12)$$

We must take $k = 1$, as noted earlier. The collapse happens in finite time inside. In terms of outside time, however, it takes forever, as we shall see.

7.3 Oppenheimer–Snyder solution: outside

The Schwarzschild metric outside is represented in co-moving co-ordinates, which we denote here with an overhead bar:

$$\left(ds^2\right)_{\text{out}} = -f\left(\bar{r}\right)d\bar{t}^2 + \frac{1}{f\left(\bar{r}\right)}d\bar{r}^2 + \bar{r}^2 d\bar{\Omega}^2$$

$$f\left(\bar{r}\right) = 1 - \frac{2MG}{\bar{r}}$$

(7.13)

To match the outside and inside solutions, we convert the inside RW to non-comoving form [1]. The spatial relations are obvious:

$$\bar{r} = ra\left(t\right), \quad \bar{\Omega} = \Omega$$

(7.14)

The time relation is somewhat complicated:

$$\bar{t} = \left(\frac{1 - kb}{k}\right)^{1/2} \int_{S(r,t)}^{1} \frac{da}{1 - kb^2/a} \left(\frac{a}{1 - a}\right)^{1/2}$$

$$S(r,t) = 1 - \left(\frac{1 - kr^2}{1 - kb^2}\right)^{1/2} \left[1 - a\left(t\right)\right]$$

(7.15)

where b is the co-moving radius of the star. The $\bar{t}$ is chosen such that no cross term $d\bar{r}d\bar{t}$ appears in the converted RW metric, which now reads as

$$\left(ds^2\right)_{\text{in}} = -Bd\bar{t}^2 + Ad\bar{r}^2 + \bar{r}^2 d\bar{\Omega}^2$$

(7.16)

where

$$B = \frac{a}{S}\left(\frac{1 - kr^2}{1 - kb^2}\right)^{1/2} \frac{\left(1 - kb^2/S\right)^2}{1 - kr^2/S}$$

$$A = \left(1 - kr^2/a\right)^{-1}$$

(7.17)

where r, t should be expressed as functions of $\bar{r}, \bar{t}$.

At the surface of the star we have

$$\bar{r} = ba(t)$$

$$\bar{t} = \left(\frac{1 - kb}{k}\right)^{1/2} \int_{a(t)}^{1} \frac{dx}{1 - kb^2/x} \left(\frac{x}{1 - x}\right)^{1/2}$$

(7.18)

$$B = 1 - kb^2/a(t)$$

$$A = B^{-1}$$

We can match (7.16) with (7.13) if $B = f(\bar{r})$:

$$1 - \frac{kb^2}{a(t)} = 1 - \frac{2MG}{ba(t)}$$

$$k = \frac{2MG}{b^3}$$

(7.19)

The matching condition is

$$M = \frac{4\pi}{3}\rho(0)b^3$$

(7.20)

which says that the mass of the star is M.

A light signal propagates according to $ds^2 = 0$, and from (7.13) we get

$$d\bar{t} = \left(1 - \frac{2MG}{\bar{r}}\right)^{-1} d\bar{r}$$

(7.21)

A light signal emitted radially at time $\bar{t}$ from the star's surface will be received at distance $\bar{r}'$ at time $\bar{t}'$, with

$$\bar{t}' - \bar{t} = \int_{ba(t)}^{\bar{r}'} dx \left(1 - \frac{2MG}{x}\right)^{-1}$$

(7.22)

At the Schwarzschild radius $\bar{r} = 2MG$, we have $ba(t) = 2MG$, and the above integral diverges. Thus, light emitted from the star will never reach an outside observer.

7.4 Rotating black holes in a cosmic superfluid

Black holes exist at the centers of all galaxies, but not of the Schwarzschild type, for they all have high angular momentum. The spacetime outside of these black holes must be described by the Kerr metric, while the metric inside should be the generalization of the RW metric with angular momentum. That, unfortunately, is unknown. For this reason, we do not have a description of the gravitational collapse of most black holes comparable to the Oppenheimer–Snyder solution.

There may be a way out, however, when a fast-rotating black hole is immersed in a cosmic superfluid. The rotation will drag the neighboring superfluid into rotation by creating vortex structures, some examples of which are depicted via computer simulations in Figs. 11.2 [3] and 11.3 [4]. When the angular momentum is sufficiently high, the vortex structure may become a hydrodynamic boundary layer that encloses the black hole, and that can adjust to any boundary conditions required to have continuity between the outside and the inside metrics. Thus, one may be able to study black hole collapse without knowing the inside metric.

The superfluid outside the black hole has no contact with the matter inside; it knows about the black hole only through the Kerr metric outside, which creates local rotating frames, a phenomenon called "frame-dragging". Here, we have an example of the creation of vorticity by pure geometry [5].

References

[1] J. R. Oppenheimer and H. Snyder, *Phys. Rev.* **56**, 455 (1939).
[2] S. Weinberg, *Gravitation and Cosmology* (Wiley, New York, 1972), p. 342 ff.
[3] K. Huang, C. Xiong, X. Zhao, *J. Mod. Phys. A* **29**, 1450074 (2014); arXiv:1304.1595.
[4] C. Xiong, M. Good, X. Liu, K. Huang, *Phys. Rev. D* **90**, 125019 (2014); arXiv:1408.0779.
[5] M. Good, C. Xiong, A. J. K. Chua, K. Huang, arXiv:1407.5760 (2014).

8 The big bang

8.1 Scalar-field cosmology

The perfect-fluid cosmology cannot describe the big bang, for it gives $\rho \propto a^{-3(1+w_0)}$, which says matter density decreases as a expands, unless $w_0 = -1$, in which case, it is a constant. And these predictions are unrealistic. On the other hand, a Halpern–Huang scalar field can emerge from the Gaussian fixed point at the big bang, because it is asymptotically free. We propose a big bang model based on it [1].

The Lagrangian density of an N-component Halpern–Huang scalar field $\phi_n(x)$ $(n = 1, \ldots, N)$ is

$$\mathcal{L} = \frac{1}{2} g^{\mu\nu} \sum_{n=1}^{N} \partial_\mu \phi_n \partial_\nu \phi_n - V\left(\phi^2\right) \qquad (8.1)$$

with

$$V\left(\phi^2\right) = \Lambda^4 U_b\left(z\right)$$
$$z = 8\pi^2 \phi^2 / \Lambda^2 \qquad (8.2)$$
$$\phi^2 = \sum_{n=1}^{N} \phi_n^2$$

where Λ is the high-momentum cutoff. The eigenpotential U_b, as defined in Chapter 5, is given by

$$U_b(z) = c_0 \Lambda^{-b} \left[M\left(-2 + b/2, N/2, z\right) - 1 \right] \tag{8.3}$$

where M is the Kummer function, and c_0 an arbitrary constant. Asymptotic freedom and spontaneous symmetry breaking require that $0 < b < 2$. We may generalize the model by replacing U_b by a linear superposition with different b's. The equation of motion is

$$\left(\Box - V' \right) \phi_n = 0 \tag{8.4}$$

where $V' = \partial V / \partial \phi^2$, and

$$\Box \phi_n = \frac{1}{\sqrt{-g}} \partial_\mu \left(\sqrt{-g} g^{\mu\nu} \partial_\nu \phi_n \right) \tag{8.5}$$

The canonical energy-momentum tensor is

$$T_c^{\mu\nu} = \sum_{n=1}^{N} \partial^\mu \phi_n \partial^\nu \phi_n - g^{\mu\nu} \mathcal{L} \tag{8.6}$$

with $D_\mu T^{\mu\nu} = 0$. The cosmological equations are Einstein's equation for $g^{\mu\nu}$ coupled to the scalar-field equation:

$$R^{\mu\nu} - \frac{1}{2} g^{\mu\nu} R = 2 T_c^{\mu\nu}$$
$$\left(\Box - V' \right) \phi_n = 0 \tag{8.7}$$

where we have taken $4\pi G = 1$.

Now we specialize to a uniform universe using the RW metric. For a uniform scalar field, $T_c^{\mu\nu}$ has the following non-vanishing components:

$$\begin{aligned}
T_c^{00} &= \rho_c \\
T_c^{ij} &= g^{ij} p_c \\
T_c^{j0} &= 0
\end{aligned} \tag{8.8}$$

where

$$\begin{aligned}
\rho_c &= \frac{1}{2} \dot{\phi}^2 + V \\
p_c &= \frac{1}{2} \dot{\phi}^2 - V
\end{aligned} \tag{8.9}$$

The cosmological equations become

$$\dot{H} = \frac{k}{a^2} - (p_c + \rho_c)$$

$$H^2 = -\frac{k}{a^2} + \frac{2}{3}\rho_c$$

$$\dot{\rho}_c = -3H(\rho_c + p_c) \qquad (8.10)$$

$$\ddot{\phi}_n = -3H\dot{\phi}_n - \frac{\partial V}{\partial \phi_n}$$

where $H = \dot{a}/a$, $a(t)$ being the scale in the RW metric.

8.2   There is only one scale

At the big bang, there could be only one scale set by $a(t)$ in the RW metric. The scale of the scalar field, the high-momentum cutoff, must be related to $a(t)$:

$$\Lambda = \frac{\hbar}{a(t)} \qquad (8.11)$$

where we have restored $\hbar$ to emphasize that this is a quantum-mechanical relation. This means $\Lambda \to \infty$ at the big bang $a \to 0$, and hence $V \to 0$. There is dynamical feedback between gravity and scalar field: $a(t)$ alters the potential V by altering Λ, and V changes $a(t)$, through the equation of motion.

The second equation in (8.10) is a constraint equation

$$X \equiv H^2 + \frac{k}{a^2} - \frac{1}{3}\sum_n \dot{\phi}_n^2 - \frac{2}{3}V = 0 \qquad (8.12)$$

and the equations of motion must guarantee $\dot{X} = 0$. However, direct computation yields $\dot{X} = -(2/3)\dot{a}(\partial V/\partial a)$, which is nonzero if the cutoff depends on the time. This defect can be attributed to the fact that the gravitational cutoff has not been built into the Lagrangian (8.1). As remedy, we modify $T_c^{\mu\nu}$ by adding a term to the pressure, resulting in

$$\rho = \rho_c$$

$$p = p_c - \frac{a}{3}\frac{\partial V}{\partial a} \qquad (8.13)$$

This is like Maxwell's introduction of the displacement current, dictated by consistency; but it corresponds to the "trace anomaly" in quantum field theory [2].

For an eigenpotential $V = a^{-4}U_b$,

$$a\frac{\partial V}{\partial a} = (b-4)V + \sum_n \phi_n \frac{\partial V}{\partial \phi_n} \tag{8.14}$$

The cosmological equations now become

$$\dot{H} = \frac{k}{a^2} - \sum_n \dot{\phi}_n^2 + \frac{1}{3}a\frac{\partial V}{\partial a}$$

$$\ddot{\phi}_n = -3H\dot{\phi}_n - \frac{\partial V}{\partial \phi_n} \tag{8.15}$$

$$X \equiv H^2 + \frac{k}{a^2} - \frac{1}{3}\sum_n \dot{\phi}_n^2 - \frac{2}{3}V = 0$$

The first two equations imply $\dot{X} = 0$, and we have a closed set of self-consistent equations.

8.3 Initial conditions

The constraint equation in (8.15) requires

$$H = \left(\frac{2}{3}V + \frac{1}{3}\sum_n \dot{\phi}_n^2 - \frac{k}{a^2}\right)^{1/2} \tag{8.16}$$

That H be real and finite imposes severe restrictions on initial values. In particular, $a = 0$ is ruled out; the initial state cannot be exactly at the big bang, but somewhere with $a \sim 1$ in Planck units. From a physical point of view, the universe could be created at very high temperatures, and rapidly cooled through a phase transition to reach a vacuum with spontaneous broken symmetry. Or it could have been be created in a broken state. There is no way to know what actually happened; all we know is that we start our model at some time after the big bang, but still in the Planck era, with a vacuum field already present.

Now we turn to the consequence of the constraint (8.16). Since $V = a^{-4}U$, it would vanish rather rapidly in an expanding universe. The same is true of ϕ_n, which is proportional to a^{-1} by dimension analysis. Thus, the constraint (8.16) would make $H \to 0$. Given the absence of relevant scale, we expect H to obey a power law:

$$H \sim t^{-p}$$
$$a \sim \exp t^{1-p}$$

(8.17)

The argument is far from rigorous, of course, but the result is verified in numerical solutions, which show that the power law emerges after averaging over small high-frequency oscillations.

8.4 Numerical solutions

We illustrate numerical solutions for a real scalar field $(N = 1)$. A multi-component field would yield qualitatively the same results. The cosmological equations can be rewritten as a set of first-order autonomous equations:

$$\dot{a} = Ha$$

$$\dot{H} = \frac{k}{a^2} - v^2 + \frac{1}{3}a\frac{\partial V}{\partial a}$$

$$\dot{\phi} = v$$

$$\dot{v} = -3Hv - \frac{\partial V}{\partial \phi}$$

(8.18)

There are four unknown functions of time: a, H, ϕ, v, whose initial values must be real, and constrained by

$$H = \left(\frac{2}{3}V + \frac{1}{3}\dot{\phi}^2 - \frac{k}{a^2}\right)^{1/2}$$

(8.19)

With our addition of the term $\frac{a}{3}\frac{\partial V}{\partial a}$ in the second equation, this constraint is preserved by the equations of motion. Numerical procedures, however, tend to introduce small violations of the constraint, making it difficult to extend the time iterations indefinitely.

For completeness, we restate the Halpern–Huang potential V, which is generally a linear superposition of eigenpotentials V_b:

$$V_b(\phi) = a^{-4}U_b(z)$$
$$U_b(z) = ca^b\left[M\left(-2+b/2,1/2,z\right) - 1\right] \qquad (8.20)$$
$$z = 8\pi^2 a^2 \phi^2$$

where M is the Kummer function. Some useful formulas are

$$a\frac{\partial V_b}{\partial a} = (b-4)V_b + \phi\frac{\partial V_b}{\partial\phi}$$
$$\frac{\partial V_b}{\partial\phi} = 16\pi^2 a^{-2}\phi U_b' \qquad (8.21)$$
$$U_b'(z) = -c_0(4-b)a^b M\left(-1+b/2,3/2,z\right)$$

The model parameters are

$$\begin{aligned}
\text{Curvature:} \quad & k = 1, 0, -1 \\
\text{Eigenvalue:} \quad & 0 < b < 2 \qquad (8.22) \\
\text{Potential strength:} \quad & c_0
\end{aligned}$$

A pair of values $\{b, c_0\}$ should be specified for each eigenpotential in V. The c_0's should be real numbers of either sign, such that V be positive for large ϕ, and have a lowest minimum at $\phi \neq 0$.

First, we use an eigenpotential with $b = 1$, which is shown in Fig. 8.1 at $a = 1$. As the universe expands, it will increase uniformly

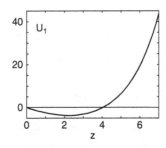

Fig. 8.1 The Halpern–Huang eigenpotential $U_1(z)$, with $z = 8\pi^2(a\phi)^2$, where ϕ is a real scalar field, and a is the Robertson–Walker length scale. The plot is done for $a = 1$.

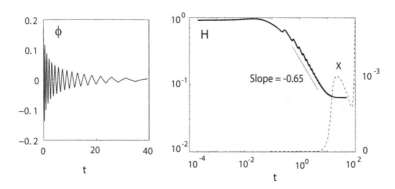

Fig. 8.2 Results from solving the initial-value problem with the potential U_1 of Fig. 8.1. The Hubble parameter H follows a power law t^{-p} after averaging over small oscillations. The flat tail is spurious, arising from numerical instability. The scalar field ϕ oscillates with large amplitudes, sampling the exponential region of the potential. Dotted line shows X of the constraint equation $X = 0$. Deviation from zero shows the numerical solution is unreliable. Note X is a semilog plot with y-axis label on the right.

Table 8.1   Computational data: $k = $ curvature; $b, c = $ potential parameters; others are initial data; $p = $ output exponent.

k	b	c_0	a_0	ϕ_0	$\dot{\phi}_0$	H_0	p
-1	1	0.1	1.00	0.01	0.1	1.00	0.81
0	1	0.1	1.85	0.17	0.2	0.91	0.65
1	1	0.1	1.85	0.19	0.2	1.70	0.15

by a factor $a(t)$. This property is a linear approximation that holds for sufficiently small $a(t)$. Figure 8.2 shows the results for this potential, for curvature parameter $k = 0$. We see that $H(t)$ makes small and rapid oscillations about an average behavior consistent with a power law

$$H \approx h_0 t^{-p} \qquad (8.23)$$

The exponent p for various choices of parameters are tabulated in Table 8.1.

Figure 8.3 shows the results for the potential of Fig. 5.4, which is a superposition of eigenpotentials to produce two very deep and

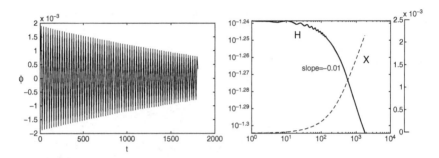

Fig. 8.3 Results for the potential of Fig. 5.4, with two very deep and narrow minima. The field flip-flops between the minima, behaving like an Ising spin.

narrow minima. The field flip-flops between the minima like an Ising spin.

In all cases, the radius of the universe expands according to

$$a(t) \approx a_0 \exp\left(\kappa_0 t^{1-p}\right) \tag{8.24}$$

where $\kappa_0 = h_0/(1-p)$. The expansion is accelerating, showing there is dark energy. Comparison with observational data will be provided in Chapter 10.

One would expect the initial value of H was of the order of unity in Planck units, because, that was the only scale. The present value of H, however, is about 10^{-60}. If H were a constant, one would have to "fine-tune" it by 60 orders of magnitude! But in our model, H decays in time with a power law, and the initial value could decrease to the presently observed value in 15 billion years. The power law decay has been proposed earlier on a phenomenological basis [3], and named "intermediate inflation."

References

[1] K. Huang, H.-B. Low, R.-S. Tung, "Scalar field cosmology I: asymptotic freedom and the initial-value problem", arXiv:1106.5282 (2011).
[2] M. E. Peskin and D. V. Schroeder, *An Introduction to Quantum Field Theory* (Westview Press, 1995), p. 684, Eq. (19.155).
[3] J. Barrow, *Phys. Rev. D* **51**, 2729 (1995).

9 Creation of matter

9.1 Quantum turbulence creates all matter

The uniformity of matter in the present universe suggests that all matter was created within a very short time of the big bang, so that different parts were within the horizon of one other. In our model, the matter must be created in our scalar field, but by what mechanism? The long-held theory of inflationary universe [1] introduces a ϕ^4 scalar field created at the maximum of the field potential, rolled down to a minimum, oscillated about it and radiated matter. Apart from the problem that the initial state was unclear, because the RG trajectory never touched the Gaussian fixed point, it has not been demonstrated that the oscillation can create all the matter in a sufficiently short time.

The Halpern–Huang scalar field, being asymptotically free, provides a possible initial-state; but it fails to efficiently create matter through conventional coupling [2]. New physics is called for, and we find it in the quantum turbulence in a complex scalar field. In the rough and tumble of the big bang era, the scalar field must have emerged far from equilibrium in a state of quantum turbulence, which is a vortex tangle maintained by vortex reconnections [3]. Each reconnection produces two jets of kinetic energy that could create matter.

As a rough estimate, reconnections should occur at the rate of one per Planck volume (10^{-99} cm^3) per Planck time (10^{-43} s), and each reconnection should release the order of one unit of Planck energy (10^{18} GeV). Assuming the universe expands with radius increasing like $R \sim e^{Ht}$, the total energy will increase like $E = E_0 e^{3Ht}$, where E_0 is of the order of the Planck energy 10^{18} GeV. The total energy in the present universe is about 10^{22} mass of the sun, or 5×10^{28} GeV. To produce that amount of energy would take $Ht = 8.2$. Taking $H = 1$ in Planck units, we find $t \sim 10^{-32}$s, which is how long the vortex tangle needed to last to produce all the matter in the universe. These estimates are very crude, but indicate that the idea is worth looking into.

9.2 Homogeneous vorticity

The Halpern–Huang complex scalar field ϕ corresponds to $N = 2$:

$$\phi = \frac{\phi_1 + i\phi_2}{\sqrt{2}} = Fe^{i\sigma}$$

$$\phi^* = \frac{\phi_1 - i\phi_2}{\sqrt{2}} = Fe^{-i\sigma} \tag{9.1}$$

The Lagrangian density is given by

$$\mathcal{L}_\phi = g^{\mu\nu}\partial_\mu\phi^*\partial_\nu\phi - V \tag{9.2}$$

where

$$V(\phi) = \Lambda^4 U_b(z)$$
$$U_b(z) = ca^b\left[M\left(-2 + b/2, 1, z\right) - 1\right] \tag{9.3}$$
$$z = 16\pi^2\Lambda^{-2}\phi^*\phi$$

The equation of motion is

$$\left(\Box - V'\right)\phi = 0 \tag{9.4}$$

where $V' = dV/d(\phi^*\phi)$, and

$$\Box\phi \equiv \frac{1}{\sqrt{-g}}\partial_\mu\left(\sqrt{-g}g^{\mu\nu}\partial_\nu\phi\right) \qquad (9.5)$$

In the phase representation the equations of motion are

$$\Box F - Fg^{\mu\nu}\partial_\mu\sigma\partial_\nu\sigma - \frac{1}{2}\frac{\partial V}{\partial F} = 0$$

$$\Box\sigma = 0 \qquad (9.6)$$

Vorticity arises when there are vortex lines, about which the circulation is non-vanishing and quantized:

$$\oint_C dx \cdot \nabla\sigma = 2\pi n \quad (n = 0, \pm1, \pm2, \ldots) \qquad (9.7)$$

where C is a closed loop encircling the vortex line. The field modulus F vanishes on the vortex line, with a healing length. Thus, F is non-uniform in the presence of vorticity, and this poses a problem if we want to use the RW metric. A way out is to take the vortex line to be a tube in which $F = 0$, and assume F to be uniform outside. The vortex tubes are assumed to have uniform average density per unit volume ℓ. In this manner, we have a uniform system, albeit in a non-simply connected space.

We average the equations of motion (9.6) over space and obtain

$$\ddot{F} = -3H\dot{F} + F\langle\dot{\sigma}^2\rangle - F\langle v^2\rangle - \frac{1}{2}\frac{\partial V}{\partial F}$$

$$\frac{d}{dt}\langle\dot{\sigma}\rangle = -3H\langle\dot{\sigma}\rangle \qquad (9.8)$$

where $v = |\nabla\sigma|$, $H = \dot{a}/a$, and $\langle\rangle$ denotes the spatial average. The energy density and pressure of the scalar field are given through the energy-momentum tensor by

$$\rho_\phi = \dot{F}^2 + \langle\dot{\sigma}^2\rangle + V$$

$$p_\phi = \dot{F}^2 + \langle\dot{\sigma}^2\rangle - V - \frac{a}{3}\frac{\partial V}{\partial a} \qquad (9.9)$$

where the $\partial V / \partial a$ term is explained in the last chapter. The second equation in (9.8) gives $\langle \dot{\sigma} \rangle \propto a^{-3}$, which will rapidly vanish as a increases. Thus $\langle \dot{\sigma}^2 \rangle \sim O(a^{-6})$, and we neglect it. Now we have

$$\ddot{F} = -3H\dot{F} - F\langle v^2 \rangle - \frac{1}{2}\frac{\partial V}{\partial F} \tag{9.10}$$

and

$$\rho_\phi = \dot{F}^2 + V + \langle v^2 \rangle$$

$$p_\phi = \dot{F}^2 - V - \langle v^2 \rangle - \frac{a}{3}\frac{\partial V}{\partial a} \tag{9.11}$$

The vortex tubes created in the big bang era must have a core radius proportional to $a(t)$ of the RW metric, since that is the only length scale available. This core will expand with the universe, maintaining the same fraction of the radius of the universe, and will grow now to tens of millions of light years, if they persist.

9.3 Vinen's equation

The vortex line density $\ell(t)$ obeys Vinen's phenomenological equation, which in flat spacetime has the form $\dot{\ell} = A\ell^{3/2} - B\ell^2$, where A and B are phenomenological parameters. The generalization to curved spacetime is

$$g^{-1/2}\frac{d}{dt}\left(g^{1/2}\ell\right) = A\ell^{3/2} - B\ell^2 \tag{9.12}$$

In RW metric this reduces to

$$\dot{\ell} = -3H\ell + A\ell^{3/2} - B\ell^2 \tag{9.13}$$

The energy density of the vortex tangle is

$$\rho_v = \epsilon_0 \ell \tag{9.14}$$

where ϵ_0 is the energy per unit length of the vortex tube. Vinen's equation states

$$\dot{\rho}_v = -3H\rho_v + \alpha\rho_v^{3/2} - \beta\rho_v^2 \tag{9.15}$$

where α and β are model parameters that may depend on the time.

Two vortex lines undergo reconnection when they approach each other to within a distance $\delta \propto v^{-1}$, where v is their relative speed, which is of the same order as the average speed in the superfluid. Thus, in steady-state, the average spacing between vortex lines should be δ. On the other hand, by geometrical considerations, the average spacing should be of order $\ell^{-1/2}$. [See arguments leading to (2.12).] This gives the estimate

$$\langle v^2 \rangle = \zeta_0 \rho_v \qquad (9.16)$$

where ζ_0 is a constant.

The parameters α, β, ζ_0 may depend on $a(t)$, for they could depend on the radius of the vortex core.

9.4 Cosmological equations with quantum turbulence

We now introduce matter in the form of a classical perfect fluid of energy density ρ_m. Its pressure is taken to be $p_m = w_0 \rho_m$, where w_0 is the equation-of-state parameter, with possible values $\{-1, 0, 1/3\}$ corresponding respectively to "vacuum energy", "pressureless dust", and "radiation". The total energy density ρ and total pressure p are now given by

$$\rho = \rho_\phi + \rho_m + \rho_v$$
$$p = p_\phi + w_0 \rho_m \qquad (9.17)$$

and the total energy-momentum tensor is

$$T_{tot}^{\mu\nu} = T_F^{\mu\nu} + T_\ell^{\mu\nu} + T_m^{\mu\nu} \qquad (9.18)$$

where $T_F^{\mu\nu}$ is that of a real scalar field, $T_\ell^{\mu\nu}$ is that for the vortex system, and $T_m^{\mu\nu}$ is that of matter. The following table summarizes the variables, and the origins of their dynamics:

Variables	Equation of motion
$a =$ RW scale	$\dot{a}$ from Einstein's equation, whose source is $T^{\mu\nu}_{total}$
$F =$ Modulus of scalar field	$\dot{F}$ from field equation
$\ell =$ Vortex-line density	$\dot{\ell}$ from Vinen's equation
$\rho_m =$ Matter density	$\dot{\rho}_m$ from $D_\mu T^{\mu\nu}_{tot} = 0$

$$(9.19)$$

The cosmological equations are then given by

$$\dot{H} = \frac{k}{a^2} - (\rho + p)$$

$$\ddot{F} = -3H\dot{F} - F\langle v^2 \rangle - \frac{1}{2}\frac{\partial V}{\partial F}$$

$$\dot{\rho}_v = -3H\rho_v + \alpha\rho_v^{3/2} - \beta\rho_v^2$$

$$X \equiv H^2 + \frac{k}{a^2} - \frac{2}{3}\rho = 0$$

$$(9.20)$$

where the last equation is a constraint. The other equations guarantee that $\dot{X} = 0$. We rewrite them in the following form:

$$\dot{H} = \frac{k}{a^2} - 2\dot{F}^2 + \frac{a}{3}\frac{\partial V}{\partial a} - (1 + w_0)\rho_m - \rho_v$$

$$\ddot{F} = -3H\dot{F} - \zeta_0\rho_v F - \frac{1}{2}\frac{\partial V}{\partial F}$$

$$\dot{\rho}_v = -3H\rho_v + \alpha\rho_v^{3/2} - \beta\rho_v^2$$

$$\dot{\rho}_m = -3H(1 + w_0)\rho_m - \alpha\rho_v^{3/2} + \beta\rho_v^2 + \frac{dF^2}{dt}\zeta_0\rho_v$$

$$(9.21)$$

where the last equation is a rewrite of $\dot{X} = 0$. The constraint on initial conditions is

$$X \equiv H^2 + \frac{k}{a^2} - \frac{2}{3}\rho = 0 \qquad (9.22)$$

which is preserved by the equations of motion.

Finally, we introduce the total energies

$$E_v = a^3\rho_v$$

$$E_m = a^{3(1+w_0)}\rho_m$$

$$(9.23)$$

so as to absorb the kinematic terms proportional to $3H$ in the equations. For simplicity, we take $w_0 = 0$, corresponding to pressureless dust. The cosmological equations plus constraint then become

$$\dot{H} = \frac{k}{a^2} - 2\dot{F}^2 + \frac{a}{3}\frac{\partial V}{\partial a} - \frac{1}{a^3}(E_m + E_v)$$

$$\ddot{F} = -3H\dot{F} - \frac{\zeta_0}{a^3}E_v F - \frac{1}{2}\frac{\partial V}{\partial F}$$

$$\dot{E}_v = s_1 E_v^{3/2} - s_2 E_v^2 \tag{9.24}$$

$$\dot{E}_m = -s_1 E_v^{3/2} + s_2 E_v^2 + \frac{dF^2}{dt}\zeta_0 E_v$$

$$X \equiv H^2 + \frac{k}{a^2} - \frac{2}{3}\rho = 0$$

where

$$\rho = \dot{F}^2 + V + \frac{1 + \zeta_0}{a^3}E_v + \frac{1}{a^3}E_m \tag{9.25}$$

and

$$s_1 = \alpha a^{-3/2}$$
$$s_2 = \beta a^{-3} \tag{9.26}$$

The five equations in (9.24) constitute a self-consistent and self-contained initial-value problem for the four unknowns a, F, E_m, E_v. The equation $X = 0$ is a constraint, and the other equations guarantee $\dot{X} = 0$.

9.5 Decoupling

In our model, matter dynamics is governed by an energy scale supplied through the parameters s_1, s_2. We take it to be the nuclear scale of order 1 GeV, which is independent of the Planck scale of 10^{18} GeV built into Einstein's equation. The nuclear scale and the Planck scale must be decoupled from each other to calculate the stellar structure without worrying about cosmic expansion, and vice versa. That is, the cosmological equations must be separable into near-independent sets, which describe matter and expansion, respectively. We now show how this could come about (9.24).

We define a nuclear time variable $\tau = s_1 t$, and assume

$$\frac{\tau}{t} = s_1 = \frac{\text{Planck time scale}}{\text{Nuclear time scale}} = \frac{\text{Nuclear energy scale}}{\text{Planck energy scale}} \sim 10^{-18}$$

(9.27)

The vortex-matter equations can be rescaled to use τ as the time variable:

$$\frac{dE_v}{d\tau} = -E_v^2 + \gamma E_v^{3/2}$$

$$\frac{dE_m}{d\tau} = E_v^2 - \gamma E_v^{3/2} + \frac{\zeta_0}{s_1}\frac{dF^2}{dt}E_v$$

(9.28)

where $\gamma = s_2/s_1$, which we assume is of order unity. In these equations, the only link to the expanding universe is the factor $\zeta_0 s_1^{-1} dF^2/dt$, which is extremely rapidly varying in terms of τ, with a time average given by

$$K_0(\tau) = \left\langle \frac{\zeta_0}{s_1}\frac{dF^2}{dt} \right\rangle$$

This is a very large number, of order $1/s_1 \sim 10^{18}$, and would dominate the right side of the second equation in (9.28). Thus, we can replace the vortex-matter equations by

$$\frac{dE_v}{d\tau} = -E_v^2 + \gamma E_v^{3/2}$$

$$\frac{dE_m}{d\tau} = K_0(\tau) E_v$$

(9.29)

These equations are in nuclear time scale. The first is Vinen's equation governing the growth and decay of the vortex tangle, and the second gives the rate of matter production. The Planck time scale is retained only for the parameter K_0, which enhances the rate of matter production — by 18 orders of magnitude.

The scalar-cosmic expansion, on the other hand, is governed by the equations

$$\frac{dH}{dt} = \frac{k}{a^2} - 2\left(\frac{dF}{dt}\right)^2 + \frac{a}{3}\frac{\partial V}{\partial a} - \frac{1}{a^3}(E_m + E_v)$$

$$\frac{d^2F}{dt^2} = -3H\frac{dF}{dt} - \frac{\zeta_0 E_v}{a^3}F - \frac{1}{2}\frac{\partial V}{\partial F}$$

(9.30)

where $H = \dot{a}/a$, with the constraint equation

$$H^2 + \frac{k}{a^2} - \frac{2}{3}\left(\dot{F}^2 + V + \frac{1+\zeta_0}{a^3}E_v + \frac{1}{a^3}E_m\right) = 0 \qquad (9.31)$$

In these equations, E_m, E_v are practically constants. The solutions are qualitatively the same as those for the real scalar field described in I, with asymptotic behavior $H \sim t^{-p}$.

To summarize:

- From the point of view of the cosmic expansion, the vortex-matter system is essentially static.
- The cosmic expansion is extremely fast from the viewpoint of vortex-matter system, but it is noticeable only as an "abnormally" large rate of matter production.

9.6 The inflation era

The inflation scenario [1] is designed to explain the current observed large-scale uniformity of galactic distribution in the universe. It assumes that all matter was created when the universe was so small that they remained within each other's event horizon, and so maintained a uniform density. The era comes to an end when, with the expansion of the universe, its size is inflated to such an extent that the matter fell out of each other's event horizon, but retained the memory of a uniform density. Traditional estimates puts the inflation factor at some 27 orders of magnitude. In our model, matter was created in the vortex tangle, which has a finite lifetime, and this lifetime is the duration of the inflation era. For the scenario to work, matter creation must be mostly completed by the time the vortex tangle decays.

To illustrate the model with definite numbers, we have to make some phenomenological assumptions about the parameters γ and K_0 in (9.29). We assume that K_0 is a large constant, and take

$$\gamma = \frac{A}{1 + B\tau} \tag{9.32}$$

where A and B are constants. This embodies the physical reason behind the demise of the vortex tangle, namely, the cosmic expansion reduces the "head wind" necessary for its sustenance. Without detailed computations, we can see that the qualitative behaviors are as shown in Fig. 9.1. The vortex energy rises through a maximum and decays with a long tail, like τ^{-1}. The characteristic time τ_0 defines the lifetime of the tangle, and therefore that of the inflation era. The total matter energy E_m is proportional to the area under the curve for E_v. It approaches a constant E_0, which is the total energy of matter created during the inflation era.

We can now put in some numbers. The lifetime of the tangle τ_0 corresponds to the Planck time $t_0 = \tau_0/s_1$. According to the power-law obtained in I, the radius of the universe expands by a factor $a(t_0)/a_0 = \exp(\xi t_0^{1-p})$. With $s_1 \sim 10^{-18}$, and taking $\tau_0 \sim 1$, $\xi = 1$, $p = 0.9$, we obtain

$$t_0 \sim 10^{18} \; (10^{-26}\mathrm{s}) \tag{9.33}$$

$$\frac{a\,(t_0)}{a_0} \sim 10^{27} \tag{9.34}$$

We can easily adjust K_0 to yield whatever fraction of the total energy in the universe:

$$E_0 \approx 10^{22} m_{\mathrm{sun}} = 2 \times 10^{69} \mathrm{joule} \tag{9.35}$$

Our picture of the inflation era is completely different from the conventional scenario [1]. In the latter, the scalar field was assumed

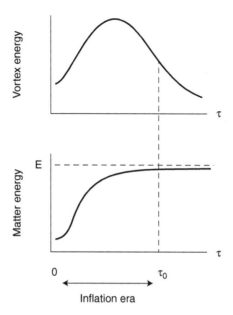

Fig. 9.1 Upper panel shows total energy of the vortex tangle (quantum turbulence) as function of matter time τ, which is related to the Planck time t by $\tau = \mu t$,
with $\mu \sim 10^{-18}$. The lifetime τ_0 of the vortex tangle is the duration of the inflation
era, which can be estimated to be 10^{-26}s, and the radius of the universe increased
by a factor 10^{27}. Lower panel shows total energy of matter produced, which is proportional to the area under the curve in the upper panel. The total energy E can be
adjusted to correspond to the total observed energy in the universe, the order of
10^{22} solar masses.

to be created at the potential maximum, and does a "slow roll" to
a potential minimum, where it oscillates, and radiates matter. In
our model, the field performs rapid oscillations with very large amplitudes that sample the exponential region of the Halpern–Huang
potential. During this time, a vortex tangle rises and falls, and all
matter was created through the vortex reconnections essential to the
tangle's maintenance.

After the decay of the vortex tangle, the conventionally hot big
bang scenario takes over. In this regime, our model ceases to be
valid, because spatial inhomogeneities cannot be neglected. However, our model leaves an important legacy, the cosmic superfluid.

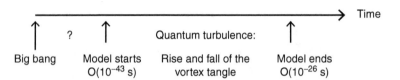

Fig. 9.2 Our model is valid only for a short time after the big bang, when spatial inhomogeneities can be ignored. This period witnesses the emergence and decay of quantum turbulence, in which all matter was created. After that, the conventionally hot big bang theory takes over, with one addition, the cosmic superfluid. All subsequent developments will take place in this superfluid.

All astrophysical event will take place in this superfluid, and that will have observable effects, as we shall discuss in subsequent chapters. The time scales involved are shown in Fig. 9.2.

References

[1] L. F. Abbot and S.-Y. Pi, *Inflationary Cosmology* (World Scientific, Singapore, 1986).
[2] K. Huang, H. B. Low, R. S. Tung, *Class. Quant. Grav.* **29**, 155014 (2012); arXiv:1011.4012.
[3] K. Huang, H. B. Low, R. S. Tung, *Int. J. Mod. Phys. A* **27**, 1250154 (2012); arXiv:1106.5283.

10 Dark energy and dark matter

10.1 Evidence of dark energy and dark matter

Dark energy refers to an unknown energy that drives the accelerated expansion of the universe as seen in Fig. 6.2. Dark matter refers to unknown constituents of the universe detectable only through gravitational lensing. It forms halos around galaxies, and contributes to their moments of inertia, as seen in Fig. 10.1 [1]. When galaxies collide, their halos can get left behind, as shown in Fig. 10.2 [2]. The combined dark energy and dark matter constitute about 96% of the energy in the universe, as shown in Fig. 10.3.

All the exotic ideas in particle physics, such as extra dimensions, have been evoked to explain dark energy. Dark matter is automatically attributed to an undiscovered elementary particle. Large-scale searches, with detectors deep beneath the earth, or on a satellite in space, have gone on for decades with no result.

Our model offers simpler explanations: dark energy is the energy density of the cosmic superfluid, and dark matter arises from deviations of the superfluid density from its vacuum value.

Our view of dark matter immediately answers some vexing questions. If dark matter were a bunch of novel elementary

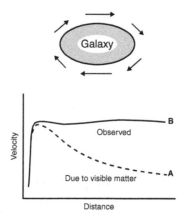

Fig. 10.1 The velocity curve of Andromeda, in which the velocity of dust around the galaxy is plotted against distance from the center of the galaxy. Visible matter cannot account for the high velocity far from the center. The missing matter is called dark matter, which forms a halo around the galaxy. From [1].

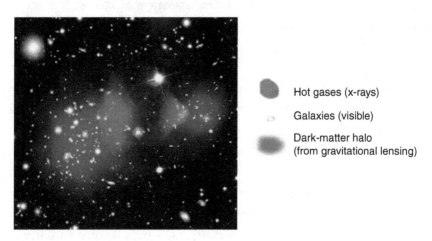

Fig. 10.2 In the collision of two galaxies, dark matter detected through gravitational lensing is seen to lag behind. From [2].

particles, how is equilibrium maintained between creation and decay? In our model, the question never occurs, because dark matter is a cohesion of superfluid density, governed by the NLKG. Then there is the question of how stars can move through the galactic

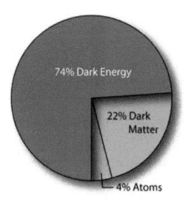

Fig. 10.3 Pie chart of energies in the universe.

halo, apparently without friction. In our model, the answer is simply that they move in a superfluid.

10.2 Galactic redshift

Our model predicts the power law $H(t) \sim h_0 t^{-p}$, which corresponds to accelerated expansion of the universe, and hence dark energy. Even though our model is valid only in the Planck era, we shall compare the power law's prediction of galactic redshift with present data. All quantities are measured in Planck units, unless otherwise specified.

Suppose at time t_0, at the origin of the coordinate system, we detect light emitted by a galaxy at time $t_1 < t_0$, located at co-moving coordinate r_1. The luminosity distance d_L and redshift parameter z of the galaxy are implicitly given by the following relations [3]:

$$z = \frac{a(t_0)}{a(t_1)} - 1$$

$$f(r_1) = \int_{t_1}^{t_0} \frac{dt}{a(t)} \qquad (10.1)$$

$$d_L = \frac{r_1 a^2(t_0)}{a(t_1)} = r_1 a(t_0)(1+z)$$

The function f is defined by

$$f(r_1) \equiv \int_0^{r_1} \frac{dr}{\sqrt{1 - kr^2}} = \begin{cases} \sin^{-1} r_1 & (k = 1) \\ r_1 & (k = 0) \\ \sinh^{-1} r_1 & (k = -1) \end{cases} \qquad (10.2)$$

Using the first two equations, we can express r_1 and t_1 in terms of t_0 and z, and then obtain $d_L(z)$ from the third equation.

In our model, $a(t) = a_0 \exp(\xi t^{1-p})$, where $\xi = h_0(1 - p)^{-1}$. Define an effective time $\tau = \xi t^{1-p}$. For $0 < p < 1$, the second equation in (10.1) can be rewritten as

$$f(r_1) = K_0 \int_{\tau_1}^{\tau_0} d\tau\, \tau^{p/(1-p)} \exp(-\tau) \qquad (10.3)$$

where $K_0 = [(1 - p) a_0]^{-1} \xi^{-1/(1-p)}$, and

$$\begin{aligned} \tau_0 &= \xi t_0^{1-p} \\ \tau_1 &= \tau_0 - \ln(z + 1) \end{aligned} \qquad (10.4)$$

Since $t_0 \approx 10^{60}$, we can assume $\tau_0 \gg 1$, and obtain to a good approximation $f(r_1) \approx K_1 z$, where $K_1 = K_0 \tau_0^{p/(1-p)} \exp(-\tau_0)$. Since K_0 is extremely small, this gives $r_1 = z$ to a very good approximation, and thus $d_L = K_1 a_0 z(1 + z)$. Hubble's law is $d_L/d_0 = z$, with $d_0 = c/H = c/70$ km s^{-1} Mpc^{-1}. So we write

$$\frac{d_L}{z} = d_0 \eta (1 + z) \qquad (10.5)$$

where η is a dimensionless parameter dependent on model parameters such as p, and initial conditions.

Figure 10.4 shows a semilog plot of d_L/z versus z. The data points are from observations of supernovas [4] and gamma-ray bursts [5]. The horizontal line corresponds to Hubble's law (no dark energy). Varying η in (10.5) affects only the vertical displacement of the theoretical curve, but not the shape. Curve A, which fits the data for $z < 1$, corresponds to $\eta = 1$. Curve B, which seems to indicate the trend for large z, corresponds to $\eta = 1/4$.

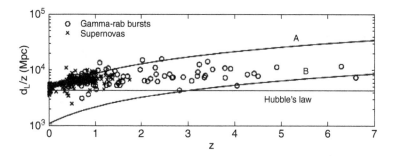

Fig. 10.4   Semilog plot of d_L/z versus z, where d_L is the luminosity distance and z is the redshift parameter of a galaxy. The two theoretical curves, labeled A and B, correspond to different values of the exponent p and model parameters.

Variations in η may come from variations in the exponent p, caused by conditions such as the temperature. This leads us to speculate that the universe may have gone through a broad phase transition, or crossover, connecting two situations corresponding respectively to the curves A and B. The transition was completed around $z = 1$. The relation between the emission time and the redshift can be obtained from (10.4):

$$\frac{t_1}{t_0} = [1 - (1 - p) \ln (z + 1)]^{1/(1-p)} \qquad (10.6)$$

For $p \approx 1$, we take $p = 1 - \epsilon$ and obtain

$$\frac{t_1}{t_0} \approx [1 - \epsilon \ln (z + 1)]^{1/\epsilon} \approx (z + 1)^{-1} \qquad (10.7)$$

Using this relation, we judge that the transition was completed at $t_1/t_0 \approx 0.5$, or about 7 billion years ago.

10.3   Galactic halo

A galaxy immersed in the cosmic superfluid will draw superfluid from the background, acquiring a halo, which has superfluid density greater than that in the vacuum. It produces gravitational lensing, and is perceived as dark matter. We can describe it using the

NLKG (3.19), in which the galaxy is modeled as a rotating source with current density

$$J^\mu = (\rho, \mathbf{J})$$

$$\int d^3 x \rho = M_{\text{galaxy}} \tag{10.8}$$

$$\mathbf{J} = \rho \mathbf{\Omega} \times \mathbf{r}$$

where $\rho(x)$ describes the density profile of the galaxy, M_{galaxy} is the mass of the galaxy, Ω is the angular velocity, and $\mathbf{r}$ is the distance from the center of the galaxy. When gravitational interactions are taken into account in the Newtonian limit, the NLKG reads [5]

$$- (1 - 2U)\, \ddot{\phi} + \nabla^2 \phi + \dot{U}\dot{\phi} + \nabla U \cdot \nabla \phi$$

$$- \lambda \left(\phi^* \phi - F_0^2 \right) \phi - i\eta\rho \left(\dot{\phi} + \mathbf{\Omega} \times \mathbf{r} \cdot \nabla \phi \right) = 0 \tag{10.9}$$

where η is the coupling constant between superfluid and matter, and U is the gravitational potential:

$$U(x) = -G \int d^3 x' \frac{\rho_{\text{galaxy}} + \rho_{sc}}{|x - x'|}$$

$$\rho_{\text{galaxy}} = M_{\text{galaxy}} \rho \tag{10.10}$$

$$\rho_{sc} = \dot{\phi}^* \dot{\phi} + \nabla \phi^* \cdot \nabla \phi + \frac{\lambda}{2} \left(\phi^* \phi - F_0^2 \right)^2$$

where G is Newton's constant given by (6.11). The parameters in the equation have been determined as [6]

$$\eta \approx 10^{-35} \text{ cm}^3 \approx 10^4 \text{ fermi}^3$$

$$F_0 \approx 1.5 \times 10^{27} \text{ cm}^{-1} \tag{10.11}$$

$$\lambda \approx 3.6 \times 10^{-105}$$

Figures 10.5 and 10.6 qualitatively illustrate the formation of the galactic halo and its profile. When two galaxies collide, their halos will change in accordance with the NLKG, i.e. superfluid hydrodynamics. This is illustrated in Fig. 10.7, in a 2D simulation.

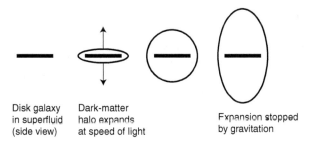

Disk galaxy   Dark-matter
in superfluid   halo expands   Expansion stopped
(side view)   at speed of light   by gravitation

Fig. 10.5   Formation of the dark matter halo around a galaxy (side view). The halo initially grows at the speed of light normal to the galactic disk, and is eventually stabilized by gravity.

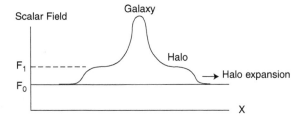

Fig. 10.6   Profile of the dark matter halo around a galaxy. The scalar field has a larger modulus F_1 than the value F_0 in the vacuum, and can be observed via gravitational lensing.

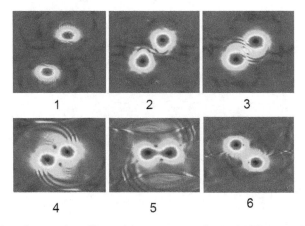

Fig. 10.7   Simulation of a collision between two galaxies in 2D space. The galactic halos "flow" in accordance with superfluid hydrodynamics. The black dots are vortices created by the shear motion between the galaxies.

References

[1] V. C. Rubin and W. K. J. Ford, *Astrophys. J.* **159**, 379 (1970).

[2] D. Clow *et al.*, *Astrophys. J.* **648**, L109 (2006); arXiv:0608407.

[3] S. Weinberg, *Gravitation and Cosmology* (Wiley, New York, 1972).

[4] A. G. Riess *et al.*, *Astrophys. J.* **659**, 98 (2007).

[5] B. E. Schaeffer, *Astrophys. J.* **660**, 16 (2007).

[6] K. Huang, C. Xiong, X. Zhao, *J. Mod. Phys. A* **29**, 1450074 (2014); arXiv: 1304.1595.

11 Quantum vorticity in the universe

11.1 Voids in galactic distribution

Our model has a very short period of validity — only as long as fluctuations in the matter density can be neglected. But it leaves behind a lasting cosmic superfluid, and a signature of superfluidity is quantized vorticity. Are there manifestations of that?

There are vortices left over from the big bang era, and there are vortices created after that, and they differ in core size. Those created in a later universe are presumably governed by the nuclear scale of 10^{-13} cm, but those created in the big bang era, before matter made its appearance, were governed by the expanding RW scale. Their core size, originally of the order of Planck length, have expanded until now, 15 billion years later, to tens of millions of light years. This is much larger than the size of galaxies, typically a hundred thousand light years.

Since the vortex cores are devoid of scalar field, and matter was created in the scalar field, these cores are devoid of matter. The cosmic superfluid flows around the vortex core with velocity that decreases from the center of the vortex tube, creating a Bernoulli force that makes galaxies stick to the surface of the vortex tube, like

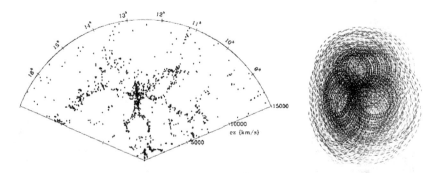

Fig. 11.1 (Left) Voids in the galactic distribution creating the "stick man" config-uration [1]. (Right) Simulation by the superposition of three vortex tubes.

metallic powder sticking to the vortex core in superfluid helium, as illustrated in Fig. 1.4. Thus, we expect to see large voids in the galactic distribution, with galaxies congregating at the edge of these voids. These indeed seem to have been observed [1], as shown in Fig. 11.1.

11.2 Galaxy rotations

A rotating galaxy with sufficiently high angular velocity can drag the surrounding superfluid into rotation. It does so by creating vortices, just as a Bose–Einstein condensate in a rotating container rotates by creating a vortex lattice, as shown in Fig. 1.5. Figure 11.2 shows a simulation in 2D space via the NLKG [2]. The white and black dots correspond to vortices of opposite senses. The black vortices have larger core size, because they occur outside of the halo. A contour plot of the phase shows spokes across which the phase jumps by 2π. Figure 11.3 shows a simulation in 3D space [3], indicating a system of vortex-rings around the rotating galaxy. This suggests that the so-called "non-thermal filaments" [4] observed near the black hole at the center of the Milky Way may be parts of vortex rings.

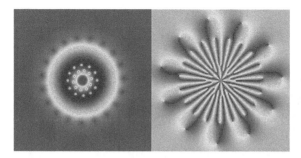

Fig. 11.2   Computer simulation of a vortex lattice surrounding a rotating galaxy in 2D space. The left panel is a contour plot of the field modulus, showing rings of vortices. The galaxy is in blue, and the dark matter is in red. The outer-most ring lies beyond the dark matter halo, and the vortices have the opposite sense to those inside. They also have a much larger core size. The right panel is a contour plot of the phase of the field. The radial spokes are "strings" across which the phase jumps by 2π.

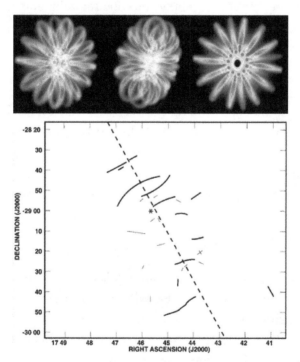

Fig. 11.3   (Upper panel) 3D simulation of a vortex-ring assembly around the rotating body at the center in various perspectives, calculated from the NLKG [3]. (Lower panel) The "non-thermal filaments" observed near the center of the Milky Way [4] could be parts of vortex rings surrounding black holes.

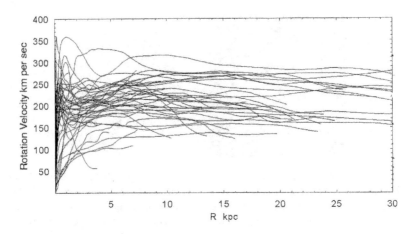

Fig. 11.4   A sampling of velocity curves of spiral galaxies. From [5].

What rotates with the galaxy must be its halo, and thus vortex structure is relevant to the velocity curves of galaxies, a sampling of which is shown in Fig. 11.4 [5]. The shape of a curve depends on vortex structures, corresponding to different angular velocities of the galaxy; but a detailed study has not been made.

A calculation of the velocity curve of Andromeda has been made [6], in which the halo is assumed to be a Bose–Einstein condensate of particles attracted to the galaxy by gravity. The model is not the same as ours, but the physics is probably similar. It finds that one vortex suffices to explain the rotation curve in that case.

11.3   Galaxy formation

A speculation of Lathrop [7] is that a galaxy can form from a large vortex ring with accretion of dust, which gravitates to form a central mass, squeezing the vortex ring into a shape with spiral arms, as illustrated in Fig. 11.5. There seem to be hints of this mechanism in currently-observed galactic properties [8].

The central mass would correspond to the black hole observed at the center of all galaxies, whose mass M bears power law relations

Fig. 11.5 Lathrop's suggestion for galaxy formation: dust particles accrete onto a vortex ring, gravitate and clump, squeezing the ring into a spiral shape with a central mass, which would become a black hole.

to other galactic properties X [9]:

$$M \sim X^\beta \tag{11.1}$$

and X and β are tabulated below:

	X	β
Stellar mass	m	1.05 ± 0.11
Luminosity	L	1.11 ± 0.13
Stellar velocity	v	5.57 ± 0.33

$$\tag{11.2}$$

Assume that the dust particles initially accrete onto the vortex ring uniformly, and then clump up under gravitation. Assume further that a fixed fraction forms the central mass, which becomes a black hole and goes dark, while the rest remains luminous. This would mean $m \propto M$, and $L \propto m$, which are consistent with the relevant exponents being unity.

The initial vortex ring may be generated by self-avoiding random walk (SAW). (The fact that it is a close ring matters little for the arguments here.) Thus, the dust particles, which initially adhere uniformly to the vortex ring, form a SAW sequence, with the relation $N \sim R^{5/3}$, where R is the spatial extension, and N the number of steps. In our case, R corresponds to the size of the galaxy, and N is proportional to $M + m$, hence to M. This means that M scales like $R^{5/3}$. Now assume that the total angular momentum J, which is a constant of the motion, scales as the galactic volume:

$$M \sim R^{5/3}$$
$$J \sim R^3 \tag{11.3}$$

Defining the stellar velocity v through $J = Rmv \propto RMv$, we obtain

$$M \sim v^5 \tag{11.4}$$

which is not inconsistent with observations. As an interesting note, the SAW exponent 5/3 is the same as the Kolmogorov exponent in turbulence, and the Flory exponent for polymers [10].

11.4 The CMB, ΛCDM, and ψDM

Figure 11.6 offers a perspective on various epochs in the early universe. The hot big bang theory [11] took over from our big bang model after a very short time, and describes the universe as a hot soup in which baryogenesis and nucleosynthesis took place. This era ends with the recombination of ions and electrons to form neutral atoms, making the universe transparent to light. Leftover radiation forms the CMB (cosmic microwave background), whose temperature, currently at 2.8 K, is uniform to one part in 10^5, but fluctuations carry important information about the early universe.

A widely used model to describe the CMB and subsequent developments of the universe is the ΛCDM model, in which Λ refers

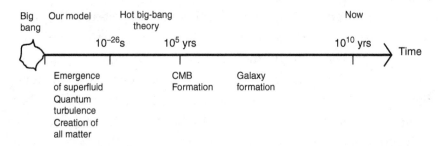

Fig. 11.6 Time scale showing various epochs in the evolution of the universe.

to the cosmological constant that gives rise to dark energy, and CDM designates "cold dark matter". The model reproduces well the observed angular power spectrum of CMB fluctuations, but the theoretical predictions are not sensitive to detailed parameters. Our model can probably fit the data as well, since a scalar field can give rise to a cosmological constant, and its density can serve as CDM; but actual calculations have not yet been made.

A large-scale implementation of ΛCDM is the Millennium Simulation [12], in which the CDM is modeled by 10^{10} "particles" interacting via Newtonian gravity. The particles are lumps of matter with astronomical mass. It finds that the CDM coalesce locally to form a web of filaments that intersect one another. The intersection sites are thought to be cradles for galaxy formation. However, such a filament structure also arises in the ψDM model [13], in which the classical-particle that makes up CDM is replaced with a condensate wave function ψ. This is a superfluid model based on the following "Schrödinger–Poisson" equations:

$$\left(i\frac{\partial}{\partial \tau} + \frac{1}{2}\nabla^2 - aV \right)\psi = 0$$

$$\nabla^2 V = \psi^*\psi - 1$$

(11.5)

where a is a scale factor. This is much simpler than the NLKG (3.19) or (10.9), but it shares its essence, i.e. quantum phase coherence. The fact that there is not even a nonlinear self-interacting term is not of qualitative significance, because the non-vanishing vacuum field ψ is maintained by boundary conditions.

At smaller length scales, ψDM exhibits novel features not found in ΛCDM. As shown in Fig. 11.7, the density structure in ψDM features filaments, granules, and solitons, over length scales from 200 kpc to 5 kpc. The phase of ψ undergoes strong and rapid oscillations everywhere. The new structures must therefore be attributed to quantum phase dynamics, or quantum vorticity.

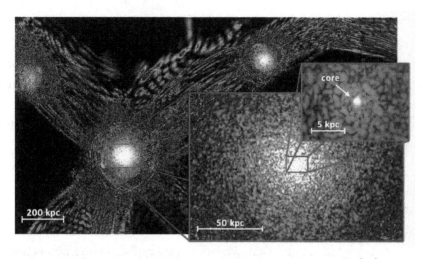

Fig. 11.7   Density structures at different scales in the ψDM model [13].   Strong and rapid quantum phase fluctuations occur throughout the space, indicating that these structures arise from quantum vorticity. "Core" indicates a soliton.

References

[1]   V. deLapparent, M. J. Geller, J. P. Huchra, *Astrophys. J.* **302**, L1 (1986).
[2]   K. Huang, C. Xiong, X. Zhao, *J. Mod. Phys. A* **29**, 1450074 (2014); arXiv: 1304.1595.
[3]   C. Xiong, M. Good, X. Liu, K. Huang, *Phys. Rev. D* **90**, 125019 (2014); arXiv:1408.0779.
[4]   T. N. LaRosa *et al.*, *Astrophys. J.* **607**, 302 (2004).
[5]   Y. Sofue, *Ann. Rev. Astro. & Astrophys.* **93**, 137 (2001).
[6]   B. Kain and H. Y. Ling, *Phys. Rev. D* **82**, 064042 (2010).
[7]   D. P. Lathrop (to be published.)
[8]   K. Huang, *Int. J. Mod. Phys. A* **30**, 1530056 (2015); arXiv:1508.05619 [hep-th].
[9]   J. M. Nicholas and C. P. Ma, *Astrophys. J.* **764**, 2 (2013); arXiv:1211.2816.
[10] K. Huang, *Lectures on Statistical Physics and Protein Folding* (World Scientific, Singapore, 2005), Chaps. 14, 15.
[11] E. W. Kolb and M. S. Turner, *The Early Universe* (Addison-Wesley, Redwood City, CA, 1990).
[12] http://wwwmpa.mpa-garching.mpg.de/galform/virgo/millennium/.
[13] H. Y. Schive, T. Chiueh, T. Broadhurst, *Nature Phys.* **10**(7), 496 (2014).

Epilogue

石洞奇文壁上符，白猿抄得左天書。
仙雲驟到慌出走，右壁真存宇宙圖。

我悟壺中真道理，蠟丸一展現方程。
源深意廓無人解，浪讀凡間百種經。

長天窺鏡盡深幽，中有玄機似可求。
物理真空同爆起，星雲黑體共超流。

White Monkey stumbled into a sacred cave,
Copied the strange characters on the left wall,
And beat a hasty retreat, when clouds moved in,
Leaving the secret of Creation on the right wall.

I glimpsed at the truth in a wax-sealed slip,
Unraveled 'n unfurled, revealing equations
Whose depth and scope seem to befuddle
Learned scholars of classical citations.

Telescopes peer deep into space,
Revealing God's great design, as angels knew it:
That Law and Vacuum rose together, and
Dark 'n bright matter co-move, in a superfluid.

Index

CPSIA information can be obtained
at www.ICGtesting.com
Printed in the USA
LVHW011326210121
676875LV00003B/110

9 789813 148451